lic. Thereafter he devoted himself to religious as well as scientific interests, and was

NIELS STENSEN's remarkable findings in the field of anatomy (the existence and function of various glands, the structure of muscles and sinews, the nature and functions of heart, brain and reproductive organs) entitle him to a place among the greatest scientists of all time. (The parotid salivary duct— "Steno's Canal"—was named for him.) He was, moreover, a pioneer in several other branches of science such as paleontology, geology and mineralogy.

Stensen's vast accomplishments received recognition in his own lifetime (1638-1686). He traveled throughout Europe, and lived for some years in Florence under the patronage of Cosimo de' Medici. In Copenhagen, he worked with Bartholin, the famous anatomist; in Amsterdam, with Blasius; with Sylvius in Leyden; in Paris he was a member of the academy of sciences founded by Thévenot. He knew Spinoza well.

A man of high moral qualities, Stensen was a Lutheran but for many years was so immersed in scientific pursuits as to concern himself little with religious subjects. However in Florence, when he was 37, he turned his attention to Catholicism, and, after many hesitations and much time spent in thought and reading, he became a Catho-

ringing a number of his w-savants into the Church. tion as a priest, he led a and, much against his will, iop and vicar apostolic to iny. Here he encountered iifficult mission field where tigably among an often un- vrote books of apologetics, y he could gather in trying sery of the poor and lived elf. He died at Schwerin in 1686.

s considered by the Danes reat national figures, and th German Catholics are se of his beatification at esting biography, already veral languages, provides ing reader with the first of a great man in whom went hand in hand.

ffaello Cioni, is a canon San Lorenzo, the Medici ce where Stensen is en- years a professor at the major seminary in Florence, Monsignor Cioni has specialized in classical studies. A member of the literary circle of Papini, Bargellini, La Pira and other contemporary Italian authors, he has edited two important Catholic newspapers and written a number of books including biographies and poetry.

NIELS STENSEN
SCIENTIST-BISHOP

Niels Stensen
Scientist-Bishop

BY

RAFFAELLO CIONI

Translated by Genevieve M. Camera, Ph.D.

Preface by John LaFarge, S.J.

P. J. Kenedy & Sons · New York

NIELS STENSEN
SCIENTIST-BISHOP
is a translation of *Niccolò Stenone, Scienziato e Vescovo*
by Raffaello Cioni, originally published by Le Monnier Editore,
Florence

Nihil obstat: JAMES A. REYNOLDS, PH.D.
Censor Deputatus

Imprimatur: ✛ FRANCIS CARDINAL SPELLMAN
Archbishop of New York

New York
September 6, 1962

The nihil obstat and imprimatur are official declarations that a book or pamphlet is free of doctrinal or moral error. No implication is contained therein that those who have granted the nihil obstat and imprimatur agree with the contents, opinions or statements expressed.

PREFACE

For very many years, indeed ever since I began to learn about the history of the Catholic Church in the Scandinavian countries, the story of Bishop Niels Stensen—Latinized Nicolaus Stenonis—has always fascinated me. My interest in this wonderful scholar, scientific pioneer, spiritual leader, and saintly bishop of the Catholic Church has grown with the study of the ever-increasing mass of information so patiently and lovingly gathered by the indefatigable Father Gustav Scherz, C.SS.R., promoter of Stensen's case for beatification, and editor of *Stenoniana*, a quarterly international magazine devoted to that end.

As many of Stensen's friends have remarked in recent times, the life of this great man seems singularly parallel to that of Cardinal Newman. Both were men of immense learning, Newman in the field of history and theology, Stensen in that of science—anatomy, geology, crystallography, etc. Both followed the "kindly light" of the Holy Spirit that led them to the Catholic Faith. Yet with their conversion and the separation it entailed from their earlier associates they never became embittered or hostile: they cultivated early friendships to the very end. Bishop Stensen lived at a time when theological controversy between the different faiths, as well as among adherents to the same faith, was taken for granted. Yet his approaches to his former co-religionists were distinguished by a charity unusual in that age and were not seldom crowned with success.

5

A few words may be in order to give a very brief outline of the life described in this admirable biography by Monsignor Raffaello Cioni.

Niels Stensen was born in Copenhagen on January 11, 1638 (January 1, Old Style), and received in his youth a thorough training in mathematics along with habits of great exactitude. Even as a child, he developed curiosity about medical and anatomical studies.

On December 7 (O.S. November 27), 1656, he entered the University of Copenhagen, where he pursued studies in medical chemistry and medical physics. Like so many scholarly people at that time, he was fascinated by the genius of the great French mathematician and philosopher René Descartes. Stensen was full of admiration for Descartes the mathematician, but disliked his philosophy, which in many ways laid the seeds for the rationalism of a later period. On April 6 (O.S.), 1660, as part of his extensive glandular research in Holland, the young student made the discovery of the salivary duct in the human head, which his professor named after him the Stenonian Duct, the title it still bears today.

Deeply interested in theological questions, he was visiting Cologne, in Germany, when conversations with some of the Jesuit Fathers of that city started him questioning his own religious position. It was the beginning of that long process of scrupulously exact, hesitatingly cautious inquiry which this biography describes. On November 7, 1667, he was received in the Church and shortly after received the sacrament of Confirmation.

Stensen published his first theological writings in 1670–71, as a result of a visit to the Netherlands, where he was deeply stirred by the spiritual misery of the time. He "quite unexpectedly found himself," says Father Scherz, his biographer, "in a lively discussion concerning the religious denominational situation, especially about Scripture and ecclesiastical questions." Writing later in Florence, Italy, he contrasted the Catholic and Protestant attitude toward the word of God and its interpretation, and the necessity for ecclesiastical authority and tradition.

Niels Stensen was ordained priest on April 4, 1675, in Florence, having prepared for his ordination by an Ignatian retreat. He prescribed for himself a very strict rule of life that he carried out faithfully to the end, and made a vow of voluntary poverty. So extensive and accurate was his theological knowledge, that only two years afterward, on August 21, 1677, he was appointed by the saintly Pope Blessed Innocent XI as Vicar Apostolic for Hanover in Germany (with spiritual jurisdiction also over the few and scattered Catholics of many other North German states and over the Danish possessions). On September 13, of the same year, he was consecrated bishop, in the palace of the Propaganda in Rome.

From 1680–83 he was Bishop Auxiliary in Münster, in Germany (with the responsibility also of Hanover, Hamburg and the Danish Kingdom), and from the first concentrated his attention upon giving the sacraments of Confirmation and Holy Orders. In his short term of office he administered Confirmation in almost 200 parishes, or four-fifths of the large diocese, and worked for reforms of every sort. He toiled particularly to bring back to good religious observance priests who had grown careless, and he employed the help of missionary priests wherever possible.

Bishop Stensen was Vicar Apostolic in Hamburg (1683 to 1685) with as wide a jurisdiction as when at Hanover. His last days were spent at the ducal capital of Schwerin. Worn out from his incessant labors and weakness and from intense suffering, he died on November 25 (O.S.), 1686. "Everybody, Catholics and Protestants alike, agreed on his holy life and death."

The body was transferred to Italy, and interred in the Church of San Lorenzo in Florence.

The more that is known of Bishop Stensen, the more one is amazed at the radiance of his personality, the solidity and variety of his many discoveries, as well as his exact and thorough theological knowledge. A former classmate of mine in the seminary at Innsbruck, Austria, Canon Dr. Max Bierbaum of Münster, remarks that Stensen's close acquaintance with scientific methods of investigation was a distinct aid for him in the search for religious truth, even though theology follows methods that partly differ from the other branches of knowledge.

Today, in various new and original forms, the relation of scientific method to theological knowledge is a subject of ever-growing interest. Though nearly three centuries have elapsed since Stensen wrote, lectured, and carried on an extensive correspondence with equal ease in Latin, French, German, Italian and Danish, his approach and his methods are now of vital interest. His immense cultural significance will help us better to appreciate what we pray the Church will come to recognize officially: that in this superbly intelligent, this humble and loving man we possess in the fullest sense a man of God.

JOHN LaFARGE, S.J.
Associate Editor, *America*

August 15, 1962

CONTENTS

CONTENTS

AUTHOR'S PREFACE

WHO WAS NIELS STENSEN? Although I lived not far from where he was interred and, although it was my daily custom to pass by the cloister of San Lorenzo where his effigy adorns one of the walls, it never occurred to me to inquire into the story of this man. Asked to write his biography, I began my task without much enthusiasm. To my delight, as I probed more and more deeply into this bishop-scientist's life, I discovered an extraordinary individual—one who was both a great man of God and a great man of science.

He deserves to be better known than he is. There was a time when his fame was eclipsed even in Florence, the city where he lived, worked and studied for a number of years. He himself regarded the city on the Arno as his true fatherland, for it was there that he was converted to the Catholic faith.

Stensen was well known and highly esteemed in the Florence of his day, and he was honored by the Florentines after his death. His earthly remains were interred in the basilica of San Lorenzo, first in the Medici mausoleum, then in a side chapel of the basilica nave. In Florence they remain, despite repeated requests on the part of Denmark that they be transported and buried in the land of his birth.

Florence was the first to publish his biography. Written by Domenico Maria Manni (1690–1788) and published in 1775, this life of Niels Stensen is a work of profound scholarship, but a bit too technical for the lay reader. Four years later Angelo

11

Fabroni (1742–1803) wrote in elegant Latin a brief biography of the Dane, including it among the lives of other illustrious men.

Nor was Stensen forgotten by scientists, especially naturalists and medical men who regarded him as one of the most celebrated anatomists of the seventeenth century, and one of the pioneers in scientific geology and mineralogy (crystallography), also as having made great contributions to the science of zoology.

In September, 1881, the Second International Congress of Geology was held in Bologna, near the place where Stensen had carried out much geological field work. After the Congress of Bologna the participants, under the presidency of Senator Giovanni Capellini, journeyed to Florence to pay homage at Stensen's tomb. It was decided to commemorate the event by a medallion portrait of Stensen with an inscription, set on the wall of the cloister, near his tomb. The inscription, which was put in place two years later, was written by the renowned epigraphist Mauro Ricci.

In recent years, thanks to the efforts of the mitred abbots of the basilica of San Lorenzo—Monsignor Giovanni Roselli and his successor Monsignor Giuseppe Capretti—Stensen's fame has been spreading. Among the many accounts published in newspapers and periodicals, special mention must be made of a series of articles which appeared in the semi-official Vatican daily, *L'Osservatore Romano* in 1940–1941. They carried the by-line of Antonio Neviani.

On November 24, 1951, in the presence of a learned audience which filled the great hall of the University of Florence, there took place an impressive commemoration of Niels Stensen. The address was delivered by Adalberto Pazzini of Rome. The following day a plaque in remembrance of the event was unveiled in the basilica of San Lorenzo. Among those present were learned scientists, Italian and foreign, as well as outstanding personalities in the civic and cultural life of the city. That evening a splendid concert brought to a close this memorable occasion.

Two years later, in October 1953, his poor remains were removed from the crypt which had become difficult of access and in bad repair due to the vicissitudes of war. In the course of a solemn ceremony, they were entombed in a costly Roman sarcophagus presented by the Italian government and placed in a side chapel of the Laurentian basilica.

Naturally, in Denmark Stensen's fame has always remained alive, but during the last forty or fifty years it has become more widespread. Proof of this was given in 1938 when the third centenary of his birth was celebrated. Men and women from all walks of life took part in the commemoration.

As was to be expected, the Catholic Danes played the dominant role in spreading the fame of their countryman. It is their fervent prayer that one day in the near future the Church will officially recognize the sanctity of Niels Stensen. Among those who were responsible for this commemoration the Redemptorist priest Father Gustave Scherz deserves special mention.

It was on this anniversary of the third centenary of the birth of Niels Stensen that a group of Danish pilgrims petitioned Pope Pius XI for permission to begin the inquiries for gathering documentation which is the first step in the process of beatification. Pope Pius XI replied to their request by means of a letter penned by the then Secretary of State, Cardinal Eugenio Pacelli (later Pope Pius XII). This letter, written in classic Latin and dated July 2, 1938, was addressed to Father Scherz.

13

"Very Reverend Father: The August Pontiff has received, together with your respectful and gracious letter, the philosophical writings of Niels Stensen and also the volume entitled *Stenoniana*.

"On this third centenary of the birth of Stensen, a man remarkable for his genius, richness of culture, and brilliancy of mind, the publication of his writings and the critical edition which accompanies it, is a most opportune enterprise.

"His Holiness is well aware that this has come about particularly through the merits of Dr. V. Marr and his collaborators Knud Larsen and yourself. It is with great pleasure that he gives his approval to your project of publishing the theological works of this same author.

"We should be profoundly grateful to God for giving us this opportunity to make known the name of Niels Stensen, who shines among us as a radiant model of knowledge and virtue. He is the bridge that unites the people of the North with those of the Mediterranean, removing any misunderstandings and hostility between them.

"In your letter you express to the Holy Father the desire of the German bishops to promote the cause of Stensen's beatification. This is most pleasing to the Supreme Head of the Church.

"I am most happy to announce that His Holiness imparts his Apostolic blessing to you and all those who distinguished themselves in commemorating the third centenary of Stensen's birth. This is also intended, in accordance with your request, for Karen Plovgaard, the author mentioned in the journal *Nordisk Ugeblade*.

"With my best regards, I am,

Devotedly yours,

EUGENIO, CARDINAL PACELLI"

14

A few more words on the subject of the observance of Stensen's third centenary. Promoted by a group of Danish Catholics under the leadership of Father Scherz, this memorable event took place at Stensen's tomb in Florence in February, 1940. There were present official representatives of the Danish government and of Cardinal Della Costa, Archbishop of Florence; Danish and Italian scientists, and Giovanni Papini, then head of the Italian Academy; also leaders of Catholic Action, physicians and scientists.

The Danish writer Johannes Jorgensen delivered a moving address, the students of the major seminary choir sang hymns, and three wreaths of flowers were placed at the foot of the tomb in the Medici mausoleum. A silver plaque was placed on the tomb and it bore the following inscription in Latin: "The Catholics of Denmark commit to the Holy Father the memory of Niels Stensen, whose beatification they desire."

This, undoubtedly, will be the desire of all those who know of his saintly life and have read his works. These have been printed in six splendid folio volumes: two, published in 1910, contain his philosophical writings; two, published in 1947, contain his theological writings; two, published in 1952, contain his correspondence.

"Beautiful is that which is seen, more beautiful is that which is known, and a thousand times more beautiful is that which is unknown." —*Niels Stensen*

I

Childhood and Brilliant Beginnings

COPENHAGEN, the capital of Denmark, was in the seventeenth century a city full of life and commercial activity, a city with a busy port, a university, and a royal court renowned for the high caliber of its nobility and of its statesmen. Here Niels Stensen was born on January 11, 1638. His father, Sten Pedersen, was a goldsmith who had married a second time. His mother, Anna Nielsdatter, also had been widowed and had been previously married to a goldsmith. Sten Pedersen was a man of means well known in Copenhagen, for he was the official goldsmith of King Christian IV.

Niels Stensen first saw the light of day during the last phase of the Thirty Years' War (1618–1648). In 1625, thirteen years before Stensen's birth, King Christian IV, a Lutheran, entered the war in opposition to the Catholic emperor of the Holy Roman Empire of the German Nation (as it had been called since the early sixteenth century). The Danish king ruled Denmark and Norway, and was also count of Holstein, a fief of the Empire. He was moved to start hostilities for various reasons: the necessity of protecting secularized church lands in Holstein; a wish to extend his influence over the German North Sea ports; and a desire to win for his son the rich German cities of Bremen and Verden.

Supported by liberal grants of money from Protestant England and by the troops of German princes, both Lutheran and Calvinist, who had lands as well as religious beliefs to protect against the forces of the Catholic League, Christian IV invaded North Germany. At Lutter-am-Barenberge he was overwhelmingly defeated by the imperial forces and expelled from Germany (1626). By the Peace of Lübeck (1629) the king of Denmark-Norway was left Holstein in fief but was deprived of the German bishoprics which various members of his family had taken from the Catholic Church. Thereafter in Denmark there was great resentment against the Catholics who were cruelly persecuted and imprisoned.

Though Denmark was no longer directly involved in the last phases of the Thirty Years' War, the Danes continued to be very much interested in its outcome. The humiliation that Christian IV had suffered on the field of honor had deeply wounded national pride. Thus Niels grew up in an atmosphere of prejudice and hatred against the Catholic Church and the Papacy.

20

Niels was a strong and healthy child until the age of three when a strange malady overtook him. It left him weak and listless. For three years, from his third to his sixth year, he became so weak that he had to be carried about in the arms of his father, mother, or some other adult.

After his sixth birthday Niels began to recover. All those about him remarked in the small boy an ardent desire for knowledge. If his father—or, as it turned out, his series of fathers—did not know how to answer his questions, Niels became angry. Outside this, he was taciturn, a little impatient, and inclined to melancholy at this age.

Speaking later of his childhood, he acknowledged: "When I was very small I took little pleasure in talking with other children. Because for three whole years, from three to six, I was very ill, I became accustomed to the company of older persons and formed the habit of listening to adults talking about religious matters rather than playing with my contemporaries." It was no doubt due to this physical state and the sadness of the times that the boy was inclined to thoughtfulness and concentration. It was also natural for him to accept the religious views of his parents, his family friends, and of the Lutheran pastors.

Niels was well on the road to health when another calamity overtook him—the death of his father, in 1644. Shortly thereafter, however, his mother remarried and in so doing gave Niels a good stepfather. But three years later death took him away and in 1650 Anna married her fourth husband, another goldsmith. This was Johan Stichman who did much to develop the workshop which under Niels' own father had attained a high reputation. Daily contact with some of the best goldsmiths of the time gave young Niels a familiarity with various instruments and tools. He knew the instruments for polishing lenses and glasses and owned a thermoscope, and also became interested in telescopes and microscopes. He came to know metals and chemical products such as sulphur, vitriol and niter, all of which was to be of much value to him later as a mineralogist.

Until the age of ten, Niels studied under a private tutor, a luxury permitted by his family's affluence. He was then sent to the metropolitan school of his native city, not far from his home. Here he had teachers who instilled in him a love of science, especially mathematics, to which he was much attracted. One of his teachers, Oluf Borch, a chemist and botanist, later professor of medicine and classical languages in Copenhagen, was to remain his lifelong friend. He was also frequently in the company of the children of Simon Paulli, the anatomist and botanist who was physician to the court and a professor of medicine in Copenhagen.

The Thirty Years' War had come to an end in 1648 when the Peace of Westphalia was signed. For three decades the four horsemen of the Apocalypse had ridden through Central Europe scattering destruction, death and disease. In 1654 the "great pestilence" reached Copenhagen. Although this scourge raged for one full year, and though many of the well-to-do families fled to their country estates, Niels remained unperturbed at his desk. Nothing could interrupt his studies.

On November 27, 1656, having completed his preparatory studies and mastered several languages, the eighteen-year-old student entered the university of his native city. Although very much interested in mathematics and philosophy, Niels chose to specialize in anatomy. This entailed matriculation as a student of medicine.

At that time the University of Copenhagen had on its faculty a renowned anatomist, Thomas Bartholin (1616–1680). The author of widely read textbooks and treatises on anatomy and medicine, Bartholin had traveled throughout Europe and had spent two years at the University of Padua in Italy, where the tradition of the practice of dissection of cadavers as the only proper source of anatomical knowledge as introduced by Mundinus and Vesalius, still prevailed.

An ideal relationship between Niels and his preceptor Thomas Bartholin was soon established. This strong bond between two superior minds was to outlast the years and ever to remain free from any spirit of rivalry.

In the course of his life, Stensen was to meet with many setbacks and disappointments, and now unforeseen obstacles arose to interrupt the peaceful pursuit of his anatomical studies and research into nature's secrets. He had been working with Bartholin only a year when the First Northern War (1655–1664) extended to Denmark and soon developed into a struggle for the very existence of Copenhagen as well as of the whole country against Swedish invasion.

During the siege of the capital, which lasted from August 1658 to February 1659, the Danes defended themselves with great gallantry. Stensen was called to the colors and joined a regiment made up of university students. He displayed engineering ability in the construction of trenches and gave proof of bravery, even heroism, in the course of sorties against the enemy. In a last desperate onslaught, on February 11, 1659, the Danes succeeded in putting the Swedes to rout, and a little later, with the aid of troops sent by Holland, the invaders were driven from Danish soil and peace was restored.

Although during this time university courses were suspended, Niels was one of those young men who found it possible to supplement official studies by other means. He kept informed through his reading of the intellectual currents of his time. He knew Galileo's inductive method in science. He studied the medical literature of the day and appears to have been very much interested in material on iatrochemistry and iatrophysics, evidences of the intensive endeavors of that time for a quantative understanding of nature.

No sooner had the Danes repelled the Swedes when they were faced with two other invaders—pestilence and famine. These ravages, no less than the effects of war, disrupted the university courses and Niels considered it the part of wisdom to go elsewhere to complete his studies for a university degree. Another important consideration that led to his decision was that the University of Copenhagen was not the best place for one who wished to specialize in experimental medicine. There was a law on the Danish statute books which prohibited the dissection of human cadavers.

To complete one's formal education at a foreign university was no novel thing. For centuries it had been the custom for students to travel abroad and study for a degree at a foreign university. Even after the loss of Christian unity brought about by the Protestant Reformation, the unity of Christian culture was not destroyed. The influence of humanist culture which spread from Italy to the trans-Alpine countries in the fifteenth and sixteenth centuries provided a bond of intellectual and artistic unity between the two parts of divided Christendom, and between the various European states.

Stensen succeeded in convincing his family of the necessity of going abroad. Armed with a letter of introduction from his friend and preceptor, Thomas Bartholin, he repaired to Amsterdam in what was then known as the "United Provinces" or simply Holland—a country that only a few years previously had won its independence and was enjoying a republican form of government.

In the sixteenth century Holland had been one of the most splendid centers of Renaissance culture on the continent of Europe outside Italy. Now in the seventeenth century, at the time of Stensen's arrival, Christian humanism had been combined with scientific utilitarianism. Here the oil of commerce lit the lamp of culture. The cities of the Dutch Netherlands had long maintained trade connections with Mediterranean Europe, and after the discovery of the new ocean routes to Africa, India and the Americas opened up the most profitable trade the world had yet seen, Amsterdam had become one of the chief emporiums of Europe.

It was in prosperous and cultured Amsterdam that Stensen became the pupil and lodger of Professor Gerard Blasius. Bartholin's letter of introduction was very useful to him, for no other family or hostelry would have accepted this youth who had need of a room to dissect cadavers of men and beasts.

Blasius was a Dane who had studied at Copenhagen and had received the doctorate in 1646. Fourteen years later, in 1660, on the eve of Stensen's arrival in the Dutch capital, he had been appointed "extraordinary professor of medicine" at the University of Amsterdam. Although undoubtedly a remarkable man, and one who has left his mark on the history of comparative anatomy, Blasius was vain, jealous of the fame of others, and did not hesitate to claim achievements not his own, as we shall see in Stensen's case.

His real name was Gerard Blaes, but since Latin continued to be the common language of the learned world—of scholars, scientists, educators, as well as of the diplomatic world—not only did he lecture, write his tracts on comparative anatomy, and correspond in this majestic and precise language, but he also used the Latinized form of his name—Blasius.

Niels Stensen also signed his name in the Latin way—Nicolaus Stenonis: never Stenonius. In Italy he was called Niccolò Stenone.

It is easy for liberty to go to the head of a young man of twenty-two, Stensen's age at this time. But this was not true in his case. He was of fine appearance, gentle of disposition, and one whose modesty was evident. An object of interest to the young women of Holland, he was no more beguiled by them than he had been by the girls of Copenhagen. He seemed withdrawn, preoccupied and unimpressionable, his sole passion the love and pursuit of truth and knowledge. Completely absorbed in the study of anatomy, he could think of nothing else.

On April 7, 1660, Niels made his first discovery. He had been but three weeks in the house of his host and new preceptor when he discovered the excretory duct of the parotid salivary gland, which is still known as the *ductus stenonianus* or "Steno's canal." As he was examining the lining of the mouth of the sheep and the course of the veins and arteries, he felt his scalpel penetrate a cavity and noted the contact of the teeth. No doubt, Stensen thought, it was something similar to the salivary duct discovered by the English anatomist Wharton four years earlier. He spoke of it to Blasius, but was given no explanation. He then carefully repeated the experiment on a dog's body, but met with only mediocre success.

Not knowing whether or not someone before him had made the same experiment or whether he had really made a discovery, he did not speak further of the matter. He planned to discuss his findings with the famous Leyden professor of anatomy Franciscus dele Boë Sylvius (1614–1672). Meanwhile, in a letter to his boyhood and close friend Johan Paulli, he wrote, without giving it much importance: "I seem to have found a little salivary duct."

He was never to attach importance to his finding. Later he called it a "little invention." Nonetheless, if Stensen's name is known today to every student of anatomy, it is because of his discovery of "Steno's canal." It led to an understanding of many other fluids of the body: of the pericardium, the sweat, the fluid of the cerebral cavities, the chest and abdominal cavities, of the fluid that nourishes the foetus.

Blasius did not enlighten the young man as to his discovery. His previous cordial attitude now became glacial, so much so that a month after his arrival Niels left Amsterdam and went to Leyden. There, on July 27, 1660, he entered the famous university and became a student of Sylvius, a teacher so renowned that the saying was current: "He who has not studied with Sylvius knows nothing." Informed by his new pupil of the experiment on the sheep's head, he made the same experiment on a human cadaver, was convinced and published Stensen's discovery.

Sylvius' praises of the young scientist made Blasius hotly jealous; he could not bear the idea that one of his own students had become more famous than he. He began to spread the story here and there that he himself had made the discovery, and called the young man a liar and a cheat. When, in the following year, he published at Amsterdam his manual of medicine, *Medicina generalis,* he publicly claimed the discovery as his own.

Had it been only a blow to his personal pride, Stensen would have ignored the matter. However, the accusation of plagiarism, of claiming for himself the achievement of another, obliged him for the sake of his professional honor to defend

27

himself at first by word of mouth and later by published writings.

In a letter written in April, 1661, to his friend and former professor, Thomas Bartholin, he gives a minute account of his experiment and finding. At the same time he called upon the testimony of Gerard Blasius' own brother. This brother, who was both a doctor of law and an expert in anatomical research, had assisted at the experiment and had confessed in a letter to a friend that the real discoverer of the parotid salivary duct was Stensen.

Stensen's public defense took the form of a printed treatise (the first of his publications). In his *Disputatio de glandulis oris* he proved that not even a year after his asserted discovery was Blasius clear about the beginning and the end of the duct, as could be proved by a reading of his manual of medicine.

In contrast, Professor Bartholin's reply to his favorite pupil's letter took the form of an epistle written in profuse Latin. It began as follows: "The learned men of our country join me in not finding enough words to praise your diligence in investigating the secrets of the human body and the success you have attained. All rejoice that their fellow-citizen, and I that my disciple, is making such strides in the study of the glandular system. We feel that your name deserves to be placed alongside that of Wharton, since to the duct discovered by him you have added an outer duct and the origin of the saliva, hitherto a disputed subject.

"Proceed, my dear friend Stensen; proceed with giant steps toward immortal glory. I regret that at the outset of your fame, you have created enemies, and are at odds with an excellent former friend. I wish that you and the illustrious Blasius would put an end to your argument, for both of you are my friends and I long to see harmony between you and not dissension. Each

28

one should be intent on promoting the good of medical men, and emulation should not give place to jealousy. There should be no rancor in the writings of scientists, otherwise the pen— in passing beyond reasonable moderation—will do more harm than good to the reader. But you have no need of my advice. I know that you are modest and mild in character, and I do not doubt the prudence of the illustrious Blasius."

However, he came to doubt Blasius' prudence later. Although Bartholin tried to mediate peace between the two scientists, his letter to the Amsterdam professor remained unanswered.

For several years the quarrel between Blasius' followers and those, much more numerous, of Stensen was continued. In 1663, the young scientist made his rejoinder in the controversy with his *Apologiae prodromus* in which he proved that Blasius was as much unskilled in anatomy as he was a slave of his jealousy. Finally, in 1664, Stensen put an end to the polemic once and for all with his tract *De musculis et glandulis observationum specimen.*

In contrast to the testy and contumacious Blasius, it is a pleasure to read the letters exchanged between Stensen and Bartholin during this time. They confide to each other their scientific observations and findings; their hopes and projects. In every line the sincerity of the correspondents is evident; they write to each other as friends, in fact, as real Christians, without any trace of jealousy whatsoever.

Bartholin appreciated the extraordinary qualities of his former pupil who was destined to leave to posterity many scientific achievements. He constantly encouraged him to proceed with his researches. "Probe the secrets of nature so that you can come upon the truth. Finally, after many glorious anatomical discoveries, if the world is not, as usual, ungrateful, one may

29

say of you, as they say of a character in one of Plautus' plays: 'This man is worth his weight in gold; a statue of gold should be erected in his honor.' If men do not want or cannot give you gold, then at least the savants will sing your praises."

Bartholin exerted every effort to make known his disciple's worth. He spoke of him to the Danish king, recommended him, and lauded his researches which one day could be of inestimable value for the dissection table in the anatomical theater of the University of Copenhagen.

At one time he wrote to Niels: "May it please God that one day I shall be able to publicly and in my own name give testimony to the progress you have made in anatomical knowledge, thanks to your scalpel and research; also for the confidence and affection you have always shown for me."

Stensen's affection for his former teacher was full of respect and gratitude. He wrote: "To be praised by one who is himself praised is true praise, and who more than you has the right to be praised for his work in medicine? Though I am convinced that any insincerity is repugnant to your upright nature, nevertheless, I suspect that in bestowing upon me so many compliments you are following the usual custom of professors toward their students. They praise their students' efforts not so much because they are worthy of them, but as a means of encouraging them to further efforts. It was no small thing that you praised me to your friends; in so doing you made my name known to all scientists. Every time I think of what you have done for me my mind is divided: I do not know whether I derive more pleasure at my good reputation or more anguish at my unworthiness. Under these circumstances, I take comfort only in the hope that Heaven will reward your many merits by greater fame and happiness in every domain of your life."

In another letter he wrote: "Since I possess nothing worthy

30

of your great affection, I recommend you to God so that He may bestow upon you complete happiness and a long life in our midst."

These letters reveal Stensen's mastery of Latin, a language so different from his own. This young man had an aptitude for languages, so much so that in his twenties he had mastered not only Latin, but Greek, German, French, Italian and English and Hebrew.

II

Another Ulysses

BARTHOLIN'S ADVICE to his brilliant pupil was addressed to one already convinced, for Stensen needed no urging to renewed effort. He detested the routine of an inactive, humdrum life, or one without ideals and a definite goal in view. We note in him, too, the utmost refinement of feeling, and yet we will find him impassively dissecting the cadavers of men and women in pursuit of scientific data. The same quest for knowledge was also to lead him in the next few years to travel along bandit-infested roads and through war-torn regions.

After his discovery of the parotid salivary duct, Stensen

strenuously pursued his researches and studies of the glands and made other important discoveries.

Let us see what Dr. Adalberto Pazzini, a noted Roman scientist of our day, says on this subject: "At that time it was believed that the secretions of the glands proceeded directly from the thoracic duct. Stensen denied this and affirmed, as is held in modern times, that the secretion comes from the arterial blood, a function regulated by the action of the nerves.

"All the glands are subject to the influence of the nerves, our anatomist declared. The breasts secrete milk in this manner, as do the lacrymal glands. Moreover, it is not true that the latter are the outlet for tears which come from the brain, as was believed prior to Stensen's observations. Even Wharton, the celebrated anatomist, shared this erroneous conviction.

"The ensemble of these observations and discoveries was published in 1664. However, two years earlier, in 1662, Stensen, while studying the anatomy of the face, noted the minute secretory ducts of the lacrymal glands and gave an accurate account of the whole lacrymal system. He proved that the physiological function of tears is to maintain the humidity of the eye and of the eyelid. Shortly before he had seen the numerous glands of the mucous membranes of the nose, gums, and throat. Furthermore, he declared that the skin is furnished with glands to assure its necessary humidity."

In a letter dated August 26, 1662, Stensen informed Bartholin of researches he was making on the heart. It had been held up to that time that the heart was the seat of the soul, the source of vital warmth, the throne of love—a belief celebrated by the great poets and musicians down through the years. Stensen's many dissections proved there is nothing in the heart which cannot be found in the muscles!

33

It took courage on his part to oppose the views so generally held in his day. "For the heart to descend from its place as the inspiration of so much poetic fantasy to the banality of the vulgar muscle was a great distance," writes Pazzini, "and consequently the Danish anatomist's declaration aroused much indignation.

"However that may be, Stensen had dissected and seriously studied the cardiac muscle. He had observed the course of its fibrils, their revolution and torsion, and up to a certain point he had an intuition of its auto-excitation and the possibility of its revivification."

From his study of the heart, Stensen passed on to that of all the muscles. In April 1663, he wrote to Bartholin: "I am deep in the study of the heart and the muscles, and I hope soon to finish the account I am writing of both, together with diagrams, provided I am given sufficient time for this work."

Bartholin hastened to reply: "Your observations of the muscles and heart are truly admirable, and are worthy of publication. The spirit of Hippocrates will sing your praises for your splendid observations on the heart whereby you demonstrate that it is really a muscle." It should be noted here that Hippocrates was the first to write that the heart is a muscle, but his opinion had not been accepted, and had long since been forgotten.

In accordance with Bartholin's suggestion, in 1664, Stensen published at Leyden the discoveries he had made in the field of the glandular and muscular systems under the title *De musculis et glandulis observationum specimen.*

At the same time he published his first zoological paper in the proper sense as an addendum to the above tract. In this paper he gives us the results of his dissection of two rays: he describes the system of ampulary tubes on the snout, which

34

was subsequently described in more detail by his pupil Lorenzini. Further, he describes the structure of the gills, pointing out that they were constructed in such a manner that the water could pass only one way, thus securing a constant supply of new water.

Stensen was of the opinion that in breathing the rays use water as animals with lungs use air; in a way a quite modern view more than a century before the discovery of oxygen. The conclusion of this paper is most interesting, for in comparing animals and fishes, he points out that the same function can be carried out in different parts of the animal kingdom by different organs and in different ways.

His discoveries in myology and zoology were to be further developed. The former in the opus entitled *Elementorum myologiae specimen seu musculi descriptio geometrica,* and the latter in the form of a supplement entitled *Canis carchariae dissectum caput,* published in Florence in 1667.

But we are anticipating. Let us remain a little while longer in the Dutch Netherlands.

As if this were possible! Stensen never remained long anchored in one place. While a student at Leyden, he and some friends made summer tours which took them through various provinces of Holland; also through Belgium and France. A modern Ulysses, he wished to see new countries, new people new customs. He wanted to meet and consult renowned scientists so that he could become more knowledgeable. Sometimes he undertook a work of mercy and attended friends and other sick persons in the capacity of physician.

Was he, perhaps, in search of distraction? Never. We know that he preferred the studious life of reflection and silence; he sought out the company of mature men rather than that of the young and boisterous. He himself tells us: "In my travels, I avoided the company of idle people, and always sought the acquaintance and friendship of those who were known for their good deeds and for their knowledge. In addition, God had accorded me certain intuitions in the realm of the natural sciences which seemed to interest cultivated and learned men. There were also many devout people who, knowing of my studies in the natural sciences, sought me out in order to discuss supernatural matters and to have me explain nature's secrets to them. It seemed as though God, having enriched me with natural gifts, was preparing me to receive supernatural graces by means of the friendships I made. It thus happened that in the course of my travels, I conversed with many people, sometimes in very confidential terms, and came to know men who, notwithstanding their preoccupation with science, had time for prayer; I felt a certain veneration for them."

Among the friends Stensen made at the University of Leyden were two fellow-students in whose company he spent his holidays traveling about Europe: Jan Swammerdam (1637–1680), a Dutchman; and Theodor Kerckring (1639–1693), a German. The former became a great anatomist and the greatest entomologist of his time. He made a study of 3,000 insects and carefully described the life history of certain insects from the caterpillar stage to maturity and compared the change of tadpole into frog with the development of the human embryo. Kerckring also left his mark on anatomical studies. After visiting Italy in 1679, he returned to his native Hamburg and made that free imperial city of North Germany his permanent home, serving there for some years as special envoy of the Grand Duke of Tuscany.

The mentality of the new bourgeois culture which prevailed in Holland at this time was that of toleration on a rationalistic basis. The historical process leading to this climate of toleration had its roots not in Protestantism, but in Socinianism—derived from a group of "supernatural rationalists" headed by two Florentine refugees, Lelio Sozzini, or Socinus, and his nephew Faustus Socinus.

Socinianism with its evangelical rationalism and the theory of political toleration, combined with an assortment of humanistic notions of naturalism and rationalism emanating from Renaissance Italy, crept into the world of culture, and into the formation of the mind of the seventeenth century.

The University of Leyden was a stronghold of Socinianism, and for the first time Stensen found himself shaken in his orthodox Lutheran convictions. For a time he was attracted to Cartesianism which in the midst of the uncertainties around him seemed to offer a certain philosophy of life.

René Descartes Dupperron, popularly known as Descartes (1596–1650), was born in Touraine, France, and educated by the Jesuits at the College of La Flèche where he got a thorough grounding in mathematics. At the early age of twenty-three he formulated analytical geometry. He then spent a year in Italy where he pursued scientific studies. Later he went to Holland and lived there for twenty years (1629–1649) except for a few brief visits to France and England.

Descartes believed that it was possible for the mind to deduce from a few abstract principles a great *summa* of knowledge. The whole body of sciences (including metaphysics, sometimes called fundamental philosophy) was to be erected on a mathematical basis according to the ancient Pythagorean-Platonic tradition.

Descartes sought an explanation of all reality following the mathematical method of pure deduction. As he himself informs us in his *Rules for the Guidance of Our Native Powers*,

37

his methodology consists in starting with simple self-evident truths or axioms, as in geometry, and then reasoning from them to particular conclusions.

In order to give mathematics the primacy among the sciences, he denied that science has a double object—namely, *what* is studied and *how* it is studied, or the object which science studies—and concentrated on method.

In enthroning mathematics as the supreme science not only did he invert the relation between ideas and things by making ideas precede in cognition, he reduced metaphysics to a science all of whose propositions could be deduced from clear ideas in mathematical fashion as they are in geometry.

The whole universe, except God and the rational soul, were viewed by Descartes as mechanical. His attempt to understand organic as well as inorganic operations in mechanical terms gave a reckless but fruitful impetus to biology and physiology.

Theologians in the universities of Utrecht and Leyden saw in Descartes' mechanical cosmogony a descent to within a step of atheism. If the universe could get along with merely an initial impetus from God, it was only a matter of time till God would be absolved from that initial push. Descartes would have been persecuted but for the intervention of the French ambassador and the Prince of Orange who held the hereditary office of stadholder, or governor-general, of the Dutch Netherlands.

The disciples of Descartes did not merely propagate their master's philosophy as it came from his mind. They modified his teachings and gave a new development to his principles. One of the most famous of these developments of Cartesian principles is known in the history of thought as the pantheism of Spinoza.

Baruch or Benedict Spinoza, or De Spinoza, was born at Amsterdam in 1634, and died at The Hague in 1677. (He was Stensen's senior by four years.) Spinoza's parents were of Jewish-Portuguese extraction. Brought up in the Hebrew faith, he was expelled from the Jewish community on account of his "frightful heresies." He lived quietly under the roof of a Calvinist landlady, pursued his philosophical studies, expounded his pantheistic doctrine in two of his works, and supported himself by the polishing of lens.

In the Old Testament we read that God created heaven and earth, hence God and His creation are distinct. Descartes admitted three substances—God and mind and matter. God was, in a sense, more substantial than mind and matter, since He created them, and could, if He chose, annihilate them.

Spinoza took as his starting point Descartes' definition of substance, i.e., a thing which exists in such a way as to stand in need of nothing beyond itself in order to exist. From this definition of substance he concluded that there is only one substance in all existence, and this single substance is God or Nature. Hence "I" or "you" can have no individual separate existence outside this divine substance. It answers the question: "What am I?" by asserting that we are all only phases or aspects of the pantheistic divinity. "You" and "I" are but so many tiny wavelets on the great ocean of substance; we roll our little course, and sink to rise no more.

Spinoza taught there is no freedom of the will because human beings are merged with the divine substance. There is no immortality of the soul because there is no soul existing in itself outside God. There is no God independent of the universe and no creation. Spinoza, like Descartes, longed to reduce metaphysics to mathematical form.

It seems that during his student days in Holland, Stensen was on very friendly terms with Spinoza. Although at first drawn to Cartesian philosophy and its interpretation by this disciple, Stensen made certain experiments in anatomy which disproved certain of Descartes' statements in the field of that science, and he came to the conclusion: "If these simple experiments break down the ingenuous systems of these great minds, what assurance do I have regarding their other subtleties? I mean to say, if in material and clearly demonstrable matters, they are so mistaken, what assurance can they give me of not being mistaken when they deal with God and the soul?"

Despite this, Stensen seems to have had no break with Spinoza. Even after his conversion to the Catholic faith and the circulation of a letter among a group of friends (1671) in which he exposes the flaws and weaknesses of Cartesian philosophy as formulated by Spinoza, he calls him "a man who was very familiar to me, and now, I hope, not my enemy." The words that follow reveal the mutual esteem that the two men had had for each other: "I am persuaded that the remembrance of our former friendship will keep alive our reciprocal affection."

But this was not to be, for as all things fade so did the friendship between Stensen and Spinoza fade away.

While still at Leyden, Niels sustained a painful loss. In November, 1663, his second stepfather, Johan Stichman, died. The following June, Niels' mother followed her fourth husband to the grave. Both were entombed, as were other members of their family, in St. Nikolaj's church, Copenhagen.

From April, 1663, to June, 1688, we have no letter penned by Niels. We must rely solely on other sources of information. From these we learn that he went home without completing the requirements for the doctorate from the University of

Leyden. There was the goldsmith's shop to be disposed of after his stepfather's death; the family estate to be settled between himself and Anna, his only remaining sister, after their mother's death.

While engaged in settling these family affairs, he found time to apply for a position on the faculty of the University of Copenhagen. Despite his scientific discoveries and other high qualifications, the vacancy was filled by another young man, Jacobaeus by name. Though academically he was Niels' inferior, his connections were more important, for he was none other than a nephew of Thomas Bartholin.

Hurt to the core, Stensen left Denmark and returned to Holland. Stopping first at Amsterdam he then proceeded to Leyden. There he discussed the matter of his dissertation for the doctorate with his mentor and friend Sylvius. He then left for Paris in the company of his friend Swammerdam.

What prompted Stensen to leave Leyden and go to Paris we do not know, nor do we know what impeded his return to receive in person the degree he had studied for with so much diligence. All the documents at the University of Leyden tell us is that Stensen was prevented for serious reasons from leaving Paris to defend his thesis for the doctorate and requested that the degree be conferred on him *in absentia*.

Sylvius came to his aid, informing the academic senate that the learned candidate had been examined the previous year by the professors of the faculty of medicine who found him completely deserving of the highest degree in medicine; that more than once he had engaged in public disputation to the admiration of all; finally, that his published writings gave proof of his extraordinary erudition.

With the consent of the faculty of medicine and after receiving the testimony of other professors familiar with the

41

candidate's qualifications, the senate decreed that in Stensen's case the degree requested might be conferred. Thus on December 4, 1664, he was granted the diploma of doctor of medicine from the University of Leyden.

In his modesty Stensen never used the title. We only seldom read that he practiced as a physician; his special endeavor remained purely scientific.

Paris in the seventeenth century basked in the glory of the "Sun King," Louis XIV. Despotic and proud to the ultimate degree, Louis would have had himself adored—so wrote Saint Simon—and he would have found those who would have adored him, had he not been afraid of the devil, a fear predicated on his belief in God, a belief which remained steadfast despite the grave moral disorder in which he lived. The religion of France was Catholic in union with Rome and the See of St. Peter. By the Edict of Nantes (1598), which was confirmed by Richelieu's "edict of grace" (June 28, 1629), Protestants were granted complete freedom of conscience and equal citizenship with Catholics.

During the fourteen months that Stensen and Swammerdam lived in France, they had no direct relations with the royal court. They stayed at the house of Melchisédec Thévenot (1620–1692), to whom they had come highly recommended. A very learned man, Thévenot was fond of learned company. A linguist and a lover of the arts and sciences, he had traveled extensively. He admired Italy, having resided at Genoa in 1645, and from 1652 to 1655 at Rome where Italian scholars were immersed in the study of the exact sciences. In 1684, he was appointed director of the Bibliothèque Royale.

After his return from Italy and perhaps inspired by the example of the Accademia dei Lincei (Academy of the Lynx-Eyed) in Rome and other scientific and literary associations in Italy as well as in other Western European capitals, Thévenot had organized in his home a private academy which became in a way the forerunner of the French Academy of Sciences established by Colbert in 1666, at the instance of King Louis XIV.

To these learned men Stensen was able to explain the anatomical discoveries which he made as he continued his investigations and dissections in Thévenot's house.

One day he aroused particular attention and astonishment by a lecture he gave on the anatomy of the brain. He began as follows: "Gentlemen, instead of promising to satisfy your curiosity on the anatomy of the brain, I will begin by saying frankly before you all that I know nothing about it. I wish to remain the only person to say this of myself, because, given time, I hope to profit from the knowledge of others. It would be of great benefit to mankind if this organ, the most delicate of all and one subject to frequent and dangerous maladies, could be as well known as many philosophers and anatomists imagine. Rare are those who approach Sylvius in his sincerity, for although he has studied the subject more thoroughly than many another, he has always expressed his doubts regarding any conclusions. Far more numerous are those who have made no such investigations and yet speak authoritatively on the history of the brain and the arrangement of its parts with the same assurance as though they had been present at the construction of this marvelous machine and knew the design of the great Artisan. Although there are many such orators and I am not qualified to speak regarding the motives of others, I am nevertheless persuaded that those who seek real and solid knowledge can find no satisfaction in what has been written up to this time on the subject of the brain. There is no doubt it is the principal organ of our soul and the medium through which its most remarkable actions are carried out."

Then launching forth into his subject, Stensen gave his criticism of the Cartesian ideas. As Pazzini points out, he did not refute the theories of others in a spirit of carping criticism or contradiction, but as an objective research scholar. At the same time he laid down important principles for the direction of future studies concerning the brain and gave indications of the technique for dissection which is still in use today.

The lecture led to much discussion. That versatile scholar Jean Chapelain (1595–1674) wrote to a friend interested in anatomy: "It has been a great loss to you to be absent during these last months: the Dane Stensen performed a number of anatomical demonstrations never before seen. These have caused those dogmatic Cartesians to acknowledge the error of their patriarch in regard to brain physiology. . . . But this is not the only reason on which is based our admiration of the Dane. Before he departs from our midst we must try to have him leave us a treatise on his new discoveries, accompanied by diagrams for greater clearness. There is no doubt that Stensen surpasses everyone—those of antiquity as well as those of modern times—in his knowledge of anatomy. And since he has not yet attained his thirtieth birthday, we can expect many more discoveries about the human body that will help our medical studies."

In point of fact, Stensen was but twenty-seven years old, and in so short a time he had already attained such renown.

In Thévenot's house Stensen came in contact with the most outstanding scientific and literary men of Paris. Among them were Catholic prelates and laymen who were profoundly religious.

At that time the most celebrated French churchman was Jacques Bénigne Bossuet (1627–1704), preacher in ordinary to Louis XIV, and later Bishop of Meaux. Whether it was at Thévenot's house or elsewhere it is not certain, but we know that Stensen met Bossuet and they had conversations on the subject of religion and the Catholic Church. But nothing came of it. Stensen felt no need to modify the religious ideas he had held since his Lutheran childhood and to which he still adhered without attempting to re-examine them. It annoyed him to have anyone suggest doubts to him or to shake the security of his beliefs—in fact in any way to distract him from the pursuit of his anatomical studies. For the time being he was completely absorbed in his search for the truth regarding the human body. Afterward—who knew? Perhaps he would then consider spiritual problems. But when he was engaged in one thing, he gave himself over to it entirely and wanted to think of nothing else.

The Bishop of Meaux was much saddened to see a young man of such high moral caliber and brilliant intellectual attainments "remain in the errors of Lutheranism." After a last fruitless conversation when Stensen refused to enter into discussion and tried to change the subject, Bossuet said with a sigh: "I had hoped to convince you. It is not yet the hour of grace, I shall pray for you often." To which Stensen replied: "I am indeed grateful, Monseigneur. I must confess I have never found so many good people as among Catholics."

Earlier, in Cologne, when he was on his way to Paris, he had met a Jesuit who had tried to change his religious views, and who had begun by pointing out to him the Christlike lives lived by many people in the Catholic Church. Stensen had been

45

impressed by this, but did not wish to pursue the conversation, although at that time he had promised himself one day to re-examine his articles of faith.

In the French capital Stensen gained admittance to the school of medicine of the University of Paris, but he steered clear of the headquarters of the faculty of theology. He wanted no part of the dispute which continued to rage between the learned men of the Sorbonne and the Jansenists who had possessed themselves of a sort of hermitage and nunnery at Port-Royal in the vicinity of Paris.

Jansenism took its name and much of its rigorous teachings from the Flemish bishop Cornelius Jansen (1585–1638). To oversimplify an enormously difficult question, the Jansenists took the position that man's fall had made his will a hopelessly damaged instrument, and that he could only follow whichever inclinations were strongest. God's grace was an irresistible upward pull, given only to the few at God's pleasure, and susceptible of withdrawal. This, perhaps, explains the rigorous regime the Jansenists imposed on themselves to attain and keep grace.

The resemblance of Jansenism to Calvinism on account of its insistence on conversion by the will of God, that is, predestination, which might almost be called an affirmation against the freedom of the will, brought it into violent conflict with the Jesuits who defended belief in freedom of the will.

In the ensuing battle of words the Jansenists accused the Jesuits of laxity. They said that the Jesuits, in their efforts to reconquer Europe for Catholicism, had made things too easy for the world and its weaknesses. Especially did they attack the Jesuits for the liberal, more humane casuistical decisions of their theologians.

The word "casuist" was stupidly given a bad name. It simply

means the application of morals to a particular case, and especially a difficult case. For instance, the commandment of God forbids us to kill our fellow men. However, there are cases in which, in spite of this commandment, one may kill his fellow man: in self-defense, in a just war, as a wise punishment.

At the instance of the French Assembly of Clergy, Jansenism was condemned by Pope Innocent X in 1653. But the movement took on new life and the quarrel between Jansenism and the Jesuits was transferred from Paris to the whole world of culture when Blaise Pascal, a famous mathematician and experimenter in physics (1623–1662), defended Jansenism in a series of pamphlets—the *Lettres Provinciales*.

The *Provinciales* (January, 1656, to March, 1657) are an example of what can happen when a witty and clever writer gets hold of just enough theology to make serious theologians look publicly ridiculous, by imputing improper connotations to the technical language of theologians and examining what they say in these special words by the light of a specious logic.

Pascal failed to understand that the higher free will is exalted, the higher the exaltation of human reason from which it springs. The revision of moral theology on a casuistic basis was merely to bring to light its links with reason. And at the same time it was a reaction against an oppressive conformism —political, religious and social—and against a rigid traditionalism which in morals took no account of the economic, cultural and professional developments of the time, nor of the needs they created.

All this Stensen understood. Whether the full realization came to him while he was in Paris, or later in Italy is not certain. What is certain is that he had been for some time anti-Cartesian and anti-Spinozan. Descartes reduced nature to a mechanism in the realization of all possible forms; like the

Nominalists, he made all physical and moral laws depend upon an arbitrary Divine Will, thus denying the intrinsic rationality of the real. Spinoza made of reality a single Absolute, geometrically deterministic.

In 1665, while Stensen was still residing in Paris, Pope Alexander VII condemned the Jansenist propositions and the French clergy was required to sign a profession of faith. In the years that followed although out-and-out Jansenism practically disappeared, the party continued to exist and hold to some of its tenets and its first rigorism. Later in his life Stensen was to combat it on several occasions.

Toward the end of 1665, Stensen again felt the need to escape from a routine existence and from the surroundings of Paris. What was left for him to do in this modern Babylon? He had met the savants and scientists and became familiar with their theories, and he had explained his own findings to them.

He now left Paris and turned his steps southward, leaving the manuscript of his discourse on the brain with his kind and learned patron, possibly as a token of gratitude or perhaps because he had no means to have it printed. (Thévenot did, in fact, have Stensen's *Discours sur l'anatomie du cerveau* published later—in 1669.)

Carrying a knapsack on his back, our young scientist set out on foot. He wished to see every part of the countryside, to get close to the earth, to see each sunrise and sunset, in a word to miss none of the beauties of nature. He passed through Saumur, Angers and Bordeaux. From the last he went to Montpellier, then a medical school and a center of intellectual life. We do not know how long he stayed in Montpellier. At this time there were present there a number of distinguished

48

English scientists, among them Dr. Martin Lister and John Ray, two of the founders of systematic zoology; Dr. William Croone, one of the original members of the Royal Society; the Earl of Ailesbury, also an original member of the Royal Society; and Philip Skippon who records that he, Ray and others assisted at an anatomy lecture and some particular dissections and demonstrations made by Stensen.

It was while the learned Dane was still in the south of France that he received a letter from Jean Chapelain. A man of many parts, Chapelain had been the confidant of Cardinal Richelieu and was now enjoying the same position in the household of Cardinal de Retz. In his letter Chapelain transmitted Thévenot's invitation for Stensen to return to the French capital before proceeding to Italy the following spring.

Stensen, however, was bent on going down to that great center of international science. On February 28, 1666, he reached Leghorn in Tuscany, a free port open to all traders and faiths. In April he presented Thévenot's letter of introduction to the Grand Duke of Tuscany, Ferdinand II (1610–1670), who was then residing with his court at his winter palace in Pisa. The Medici prince received the Dane with great benevolence.

Recalling this occasion seventeen years later (1683) in a letter addressed to Ferdinand's son, Cosimo III, Stensen wrote: "From that first day in Pisa when God gave me the grace to meet Your Highness' father, now in heaven, till this day, I am most grateful for all that I have enjoyed and at the same time confused at the little that I have given in return."

Gratitude is a rare virtue among men. Stensen's soul was filled with it, as his correspondence attests.

III

"My True Fatherland"

FLORENCE, or Firenze, the "city of flowers," lying on the Arno amid its encircling hills, was already adorned in the seventeenth century with the greater number of the palaces, churches and works of art we admire there today. To the young Dane it appeared as a veritable temple of beauty, the most living center of art and thought.

To be sure the streets were narrow; the sanitation was poor; and there was almost no lighting in the streets. But wherever he turned, Stensen beheld the austere architectural grandeur of medieval times reconciled with the classical serenity of the

Renaissance, and its immediate heir, the baroque. Here he found the inspiration of rich traditions in every field of man's endeavor. Among the great poets, Dante was a Florentine, while Petrarch and Boccaccio were sons of Florentines. Great painters such as Giotto and Fra Angelico were natives of the city as were Masaccio and Donatello. Unrivaled sculptors, like Lorenzo Ghiberti and Michelangelo, architects like Brunelleschi, universal savants like Leone Alberti had left on Florence their imprint.

Above all, for many years the wealthy family of the Medici had marked the city with its beauty-loving stamp. Bankers and traders, this powerful family had branches throughout Europe from London to Constantinople. The third of these *signori*, Lorenzo (1449–1492), surnamed "the Magnificent," was a statesman, a poet and one of the greatest patrons of learning of all time. In the sixteenth century the republican city-state of Florence and its subject cities and districts became the absolutist, regional principality of Tuscany, and from then on the Medici held the title of grand dukes of Tuscany.

Ferdinand II (1610–1670), the grand duke of Tuscany at the time of Stensen's arrival, was a prince of great intelligence, an able politician, a lover of peace, and highly generous—a trait which endeared him to his people. Although the Renaissance had passed its apogee, even in this period of supposed decline the Italian genius was manifest in every field, and the new scientific spirit which had found its cradle at the court of Lorenzo the Magnificent continued to make history. It was in Florence that Leonardo da Vinci had revived and extended Archimedes' method of combining mathematics and measurements, and in more recent years Galileo had held the post of *mathematicus*, or engineer, to Ferdinand's father, Grand Duke Cosimo II.

Since he was a protector of artists and scholars, as his predecessors had been, Ferdinand II was delighted with the presence in Florence of the young Dane whose fame as an anatomist had preceded his arrival. The grand duke willingly received him at his court, provided him with a stipend, living quarters, and the most favorable conditions for scientific research.

It is difficult to picture the young man from the North in the midst of the complicated etiquette, the bows and hand kissing, the wigs and masks, the buffoonery of dwarves and jesters at the Pitti Palace, the grand-ducal residence. He later said that court life is full of perils; yet this did not prevent the everlasting gratitude he felt toward the Medici, his benefactors.

At the time of which we speak he was twenty-seven years of age. His face was somewhat long; his forehead broad; his eyes lively and intelligent; his nose a little prominent; his mouth well formed; his chin rounded; his hair blond. Most of the ladies of the Medici court found the handsome young man charming. This, however, was not the case with the Grand Duchess Vittoria della Rovere and her daughter-in-law, Marguerite d'Orléans. The former, a rigid and bigoted Catholic, held Stensen's Protestantism against him; the latter was a gay and flirtatious Parisian who had married against her will and for reasons of state Ferdinand's son and heir, Cosimo III.

The hostility of the two princely ladies was ignored by the grand duke who was master in his own house. In addition, the young "courtier" was immediately made welcome by the learned men who frequented the palace. All were favorably impressed by his broad culture, his unusual modesty and reserve, and by his agreeable manners. One with whom he soon struck a close friendship was Francesco Redi (1626–1698) the court physician.

Redi, an expert linguist, was thoroughly well read in the

classics and collected French, Provençal, Catalan, and Italian manuscripts. A very busy man, he was also a poet and a scientist. The one poem of his that has attained for him a measure of fame is the thousand-line dithyramb, *Bacco in Toscana* (Bacchus in Tuscany).

As a scientist Redi was prudent, judicious, conscientious. He wrote: "I would like to free men from the ties which blind them and tie them to the fraud, the deception, and the knavery of ignorant physicians." There were many of these abroad at that time.

Redi preferred simple remedies. "I note that nature prefers simple things; I find from experience that simple remedies are better than those many mixtures, combinations, stews, and nostrums that we doctors daily prescribe. It should be an excellent thing if we forced ourselves to undergo the treatments we prescribe for our patients. This would make us more charitable and discreet. . . .

"God, who is the fount of all good, places simple remedies at our disposal, and we physicians are so vain and self-sufficient as to pretend to know more than God; we try to complicate and mix those simple things created by the divine Majesty for the good of men's health; we concoct long formulas, and put so many and such different substances into them that even a large arsenal could not contain them all."

He had confidence in nature's power to cure: "Nature is the real remedy for all ills and knows more about them than all the most expert manipulators in pharmacies and chemical laboratories can ever know." And elsewhere: "It is not only medicines which cure sickness and drive it from the human body. Basically, it is nature and a good regime." In the history of medicine Redi's name has a place as the discoverer of the *sarcoptes scabiei*, the parasite that causes mange.

Redi held Stensen in high esteem, and he referred to him as

53

"very learned." The Italian and the Dane spent many fruitful hours together in pursuit of scientific experimentation, chiefly in biology. Redi, himself, anticipated some of the methods and insights of modern bacteriology. From one of his letters we learn that he was in the company of Stensen at the time he undertook his investigation of the generation of insects. From the villa Artimino, where the Medici had gone to hunt, he wrote: "When they brought me those animals (spiders and other insects), fortunately I had with me here Signor Niels Stensen of Denmark, a famous anatomist of our time, a learned scientist and a most remarkably well-mannered and agreeable man. He is maintained at this court by the generosity of the Grand Duke."

The same was true of other learned men in Florence such as Vincenzo Viviani (1622–1703), Lorenzo Magalotti (1637–1712), Giovanni Alfonso Borelli (1606–1679), Candido del Buono, Paolo del Buono, Alessandro Marsili, Antonio Oliva, Carlo Renaldeni. Stensen was on friendly terms with all and took part in their frequent scientific reunions.

All, including Redi, were members of the famous *Accademia del Cimento*.

In the Italy of that time there flourished a vast plethora of academies, more or less serious in their work. At the end of the 1500's could be counted more than two hundred, large and small, and it is possible there were even more in the next century. Some bore strange names, bestowed on their members grandiloquent titles and often engaged in ridiculous and useless discussions. We can well imagine that such things did not amuse Stensen, but he took great interest in the proceedings of the Academy of the Cimento, founded at Florence in 1657, ten years before his arrival, and into whose circle he was received.

An engraving to be seen at the National Library of Florence shows nine personages seated at a table, elegantly attired and wearing wigs and knee-breeches. On the wall behind is the bust of Leopoldo, later Cardinal, de' Medici (1617–1675), the Academy's founder; above it the arms of the Medici family. A little to one side, between two columns, appears a crucible carrying the Cimento's motto: *Provando e reprovando* (Prove and verify again). In the foreground are various scientific instruments.

The aim of this illustrious company was the search for truth by means of experimentation. By such means the secrets of the universe might be unveiled; they would try to discern in the writings of even great philosophers a number of the errors which led to incoherencies and aberrations. Once their minds were purged of preconceived ideas, they would retain and accept less the opinions of others than those they formed themselves and which were confirmed by the ciment of experience (thence the name *Cimento* of the new academy). It was only by experimenting and re-experimenting that truth could be discovered.

The academy members, whose bond lay in a common love of truth and not in a desire for personal renown, worked as a group, and it was a rule of theirs that the results of their experiments were announced in the name of all and without mention of those members who took part in them. Thus a book giving examples of experiments in natural science made by the Cimento, which was compiled by Magalotti and published in Florence in 1667, carries no name of any individual. We do not know, therefore, whether it included any experiments made by Niels Stensen, or what role he played in the work of the Academy.

We do know, however, from contemporary sources, that he was regarded with great affection by all its members with the

55

exception of Borelli. This scientist was jealous of the Dane's discoveries regarding the muscles, a field in which Borelli regarded himself as the greatest authority.

Ferdinand II, who esteemed Stensen for his knowledge as well as for his blameless life, often held him up as an example to his children. He refused Stensen nothing and tried to bind him to Florence by all sorts of advantages, giving him every means and facility for his work. He made him director of the museum of natural history installed in the Pitti Palace, and later appointed him teacher of mathematics and sciences to his son Cosimo.

It was due to the grand duke's patronage that the scientist was able to make anatomical dissections at the hospital of Santa Maria Nuova. To the mathematician Vincenzo Viviani, the last living pupil of Galileo, and another of his close collaborators, Stensen expressed his admiration at the grand duke's interest in science and his generosity to scientists: "He has only to nod, and all that is necessary for my scientific researches in whatever field I choose, is put at my disposal. For my anatomical studies there are various animals; then, too there are the cadavers at the hospital. This is something that was not possible elsewhere, or if possible, in a more limited way."

Viviani, who enjoyed Stensen's companionship and would have liked to prolong it as long as possible, did his best to make the Dane's sojourn in Florence agreeable. There is no doubt that Stensen did find it to his liking. Although he had come with the idea of spending only a few weeks, he now had no thought of leaving. Everything in Florence he found beautiful and good, with the sole exception of lodgings. In the beginning he had stayed at an inn; then, at the suggestion of Magalotti, he had lived at a pension run by "certain women who were, to say the least, impertinent," and with whom, given his gentle character, he could not cope.

During one of his absences from the city, Viviani wrote to one of the grand duke's secretaries on Stensen's behalf: "Since His Serene Highness the Grand Duke, with the exception of twenty-five *écus* a month, is willing to provide for his lodging, will you kindly suggest to His Highness that he order an apartment prepared in some other place for Signor Stensen on his return. I am thinking of the Palazzo Vecchio or elsewhere as His Highness pleases, but in some spot between the palace and Santa Maria Nuova where he spends much time. If there are quarters where he could carry on his chemical or other experimentations without being disturbed, I am sure he would be very grateful. In this way he would be freed from the stupid curiosity of those women who annoy him and even prevent him from working."

Instead of an apartment in the Palazzo Vecchio, Stensen was given an even more comfortable one in the San Marco Casino in Via Larga, now Via Cavour.

However, Stensen did not spend much time in his new quarters. He was often away, sometimes on the Isle of Elba, sometimes in other Tuscan cities, making field studies or collecting specimens for the museum of natural history. He was now devoting much time to the scientific problems of geology and mineralogy. This led him to the study of the earth's crust with its content of fossils, minerals, and other substances—problems which had occupied Leonardo da Vinci and other Italians and which came within the province of the scientists of the Cimento Academy as well as the practical interests of the house of Medici. This princely family derived considerable wealth from the mines and marble quarries. Then, too, Viviani, in his role as engineer to the grand duke, had gained a great insight into the conditions of the soil of Tuscany.

Mineralogical and geological interests were not new to Stensen. The family goldsmith shop in Copenhagen had given him a certain practical knowledge of metals, and two of his professors at the University of Copenhagen, Thomas Bartholin and Oluf Borch were much interested in such matters. The former had studied at the University of Padua and had learned Leonardo da Vinci's views on the origin of fossils. He had discussed their organic nature in his books and university lectures, as also the activity of volcanoes which he had witnessed during his stay in Italy. Professor Borch was a chemist interested in metallurgy and mines and was the author of a number of treatises on minerals and the formation of stones both in mountain caves and in living organisms. There are other indications that Stensen had been aware of geological questions prior to his arrival in Italy. But it was in Italy, in the years 1666–1667, that he became a pioneer in exact geology. His additions to the Medici natural history collection seem to have been in keeping with a well-defined research program, and his marine specimens, minerals and fossils to have been collected with the aim of supporting his own scientific work in geology.

While pursuing his earth studies, Stensen was occupied in many other ways: dissections at the hospital of Santa Maria Nuova; giving lessons to Prince Cosimo; spending many hours of the day and night in study and writing; attending academic meetings, holding conversations on scientific subjects with Italian savants.

On March 23, 1667, Redi, who was then in attendance at the grand duke's palace in Leghorn, wrote to Viviani: "Signor Stensen does me the honor of gracing my table morning and evening; and so I have the pleasure of his learned and agreeable conversation. Then, too, we are not idle, and every day we are making interesting observations."

In winter, the court moved to Pisa because of its milder seaside climate, and Stensen spent a good deal of time in that city. In summer, he was often in one or the other of the Medici villas —at Pratolino, Artimino, Ambrogiano, Poggio a Caino, or Cafaggiolo.

Nevertheless, despite this active life and amid so many interests and honors, the young scientist felt within him a growing dissatisfaction and disquietude. Was it because he had put in second place the One who should be first and come before all else—God?

IV

The Byways of Science

In 1667, one year after his arrival in Florence, Stensen published his important treatise on anatomy and the working of the muscles—*Elementorum myologiae specimen seu descriptio musculi geometrica,* usually referred to as the *Myologiae specimen.* It is at once the development of his earlier work on the glandular and muscular systems, published at Leyden in 1664, and a refutation of objections which in the meantime had arisen against this earlier treatise.

I have before me the original edition of the *Myologiae specimen.* It is still in excellent condition, despite its age. This edition contains two supplements: the *Canis carchariae dissectum caput* (Dissection of the shark's head) and *Historia dissecti piscis ex canum genere* (Dissection of a fish of the dogfish genus). Bound in parchment, the title page of the volume bears the Medici coat-of-arms, and the work is dedicated to Grand Duke Ferdinand II.

In his dedication Stensen expresses his gratitude to his patron and then speaks of his purposes in writing the book: "I desired," he wrote, "to show that no one can distinguish the parts of a muscle or take exact account of its movements unless mathematics becomes a part of myology. . . . Our body is an organism composed of a thousand organs, and anyone who thinks that he can arrive at a true knowledge of it without mathematics must suppose that matter has no volume and the body has no form. . . . It would be better for us, and better for the human race, if our predecessors in anatomical study had passed on only data that was verified. Our knowledge might not be so wide, but it would also be less dangerous; and if medicine, even when based on sure principles, might not succeed in curing pain, at least it would not add new sufferings. Often when we believe we are alleviating pain, we are doing the most damage—and this is our greatest misfortune."

Again to quote Professor Pazzini: "Stensen lived at a time when two new principles—iatrochemistry and iatromechanics —were being developed for the interpretation of biological phenomena. The first was originally applied by Paracelsus (the name adopted by the Swiss physician Theophrastus von Hohenheim, 1493?–1541) to the interpretation of chemistry and was the beginning of modern chemical biology. The second had Leonardo da Vinci as its precursor and was developed in Italy by Galileo.

"Stensen made himself the disciple of the latter in his concept of the geometrical description of the muscles with its implied mechanistic principles. He was certainly influenced by Borelli and perhaps somewhat by Descartes.

"His work concerning the muscles was of fundamental value at that time; his special contribution was their mechanistic explanation. Professor Franceschini, in a recently published work on this question, shows this clearly.

"In fact Stensen was the first to give the foundation of experimentation to the study of muscular fibers, to describe their histology and to explain the phenomena of contraction. He made more understandable the lines of strength particular to each muscle and gave a better definition of the action of different muscular groups. He proves the constancy of volume in spite of contraction, and establishes that it is the fibers and not the sinews which are the contractible elements.

"Thus, in his studies in the field of mechanics the muscles seem to have been, in anatomy, his favored subject. He showed that the tongue, previously held to be a gland, was a muscle; he described the crossed muscular fibers of the esophagus, and gave their names to the muscles at the sides; he proved that the contraction of a muscle may be provoked not only by exciting the nerve but by direct action on its substance."

At the end of his treatise, Stensen showed how much remained to be done in muscular research—indications of great value for the future of science.

In his first supplements to his treatise of myology—the *Canis carchariae*—he disclosed himself as a pioneer in comparative anatomy as well as in aspects of scientific paleontology and geology. In the second supplement—the *Historia dissecti piscis* —he made a real contribution to embryology.

It seems that in October, 1666, about six months after Stensen's arrival in Italy, fishermen had dragged ashore near Leghorn an enormous shark weighing about 3,500 pounds. Its head was transported to Florence and given to the Dane for examination. The published results of his dissection are regarded as a classic of scientific observation and deduction. A development of Stensen's earlier work on zoology published in Leyden, it placed him in the vanguard of comparative anatomy.

In it he gives a correct description of the membraneous sacs or vesicules of the shark's head, and establishes the production of slime. Further, he describes the eye and for the first time mentions the optic nerve, the existence of an intersection, and explains the small dimensions of the brain and the supplementary activity of the spinal cord. Quite modern is his demonstration in a graph of the transverse sections of all nerves leading to the muscles compared with the transverse section of the spinal cord. He also gives an accurate description of the teeth and detected the auditory organ.

The study of the anatomy and function of the shark's teeth led him into the fields of geology and paleontology. This was in connection with the true nature of the glossopetrae, or "tongue stones," from the cretaceous cliffs of Malta, a problem much discussed by the scientists of the period. A few were of the opinion that the so-called tongue stones were petrified sharks' teeth from remote ages, but most believed that the resemblance was quite accidental and that they were organisms formed in or by the surrounding soil or rock by some mysterious force.

Stensen first studied the anatomy and function of the recent shark's teeth that he was examining and then compared them with the fossil "tongue stones." He then proceeded to a study of the greater problem: the nature of all bodies resembling parts of animals which can be dug out of the soil.

This study was divided into two parts: first, in eleven brief

63

sections (*historiae*) Stensen sets down exact observations of facts about fossils, namely, "the bodies resembling parts of animals," and about the earth layers. This study he conducted not in museums but in the soil and rock strata in which the bodies were found. Secondly, in six "conjectures" he logically presents his conclusions to the effect that the bodies excavated from the earth and which resemble parts of animals, "must be regarded as parts of animals." This was the first outline of a scientific earth history arrived at through inductive reasoning.

In the second supplement to the *Myologiae specimen*—the *Historia dissecti piscis ex canum genere*—Stensen presented the results of his study of a smaller species of shark, a *porcus salviani*, and again goes into questions of comparative anatomy and paleontology. He also makes an important contribution to embryology in his conclusions regarding the reproductive apparatus. Here he puts forward the opinion that reproductive organs of female mammals—in those days called testes—were not to be regarded as organs corresponding to the testes of male animals, but that they were, in fact, the same organs as the ovaries of the oviparous animals. It was quite a new view that the animals which brought forth living young produced eggs and possessed ovaries.

Stensen published several other papers on the embryology of the *elasmobranches* (sharks, rays, etc.), also scattered notes on the reproductive organs in different vertebrate groups. In these notes he again advances the view that viviparous animals possess ovaries and produce eggs—observations made in 1667, five years before Regnier de Graaf published his famous observations. Stensen also notes his rediscovery of the curious way in which the foetus of the shark *galeus laevis* is nourished, a discovery first made by Aristotle more than two thousand years earlier.

64

It seems that Stensen had planned two other general surveys of zoological interest: first, a comparative anatomy of the muscles of the vertebrates based on his numerous dissections of vertebrates of all kinds; second, a survey of mollusks. On the comparative anatomy of the muscles he managed only to publish a description of the muscle of the eagle. On the mollusks we find only a few notes in two of his later works, the *De Solido* and the *Indice*.

For the time being it is sufficient to note that Stensen made his first group of zoological investigations in the period between 1664 and 1667, so that these valuable contributions to science were made when he was still in his twenties and early thirties.

Stensen's *Myologiae specimen* and its two supplements met with wide acceptance in Italy and elsewhere in Europe. Contemporary correspondence suggests that the arrival of a new book by Stensen was something of an event in scientific circles in Britain. Scientists were not then overwhelmed by the vast stream of literature, as they are today, and, in consequence, what books were available were read widely and carefully and there was probably a considerable interchange of scientific intelligence between Britain and the Continent.

The enthusiasm which Stensen's work aroused in Italy may be judged from a letter written by Michelangelo Ricci of Rome (1619–1682) to Prince Leopoldo de' Medici upon receipt of a copy of the *Myologiae specimen*. A pupil of Torricelli, one of Galileo's most famous students, Ricci was a corresponding member of the Cimento Academy, a mathematician well known beyond the borders of his native country.

We quote from Ricci's letter to Prince Leopoldo: "It is some time since there has appeared an author as outstanding as Niels Stensen, a copy of whose latest book Your Serene Highness has

65

graciously sent me. One notes in him great skill and diligence in scientific observation, natural talent and clear vision. Hence it is not surprising that he makes many discoveries and explains them with such clarity and facility as is evident in this book. And I am happy that this book confirms what I have always said: nowhere in Europe, nor in the rest of the world, is there a place that abounds with so much natural talent, study and communication as in Tuscany."

In parenthesis we might say that at the time this letter was written (May 30, 1667), Stensen was in Rome. This was his second visit to the city on the Tiber where he had spent two months the previous year, April and May of 1666. Among others, he met Marcello Malpighi and a lasting friendship sprang up between the two men.

Malpighi (1628–1694) was a biologist and physician, renowned for his works in biology, anatomy, physiology and comparative anatomy. He demonstrated the sexuality of plants and compared the function of leaves with that of the lungs of animals. In 1660, six years before his first meeting with Stensen, he demonstrated the existence of capillaries conveying blood from the arteries to the veins, thereby confirming Sir William Harvey's explanation of the circulation of the blood.

In a letter written by Malpighi we read: "In Rome I met and talked for the first time with the famous Niels Stensen. We dined together at the Ludovici villa. Guglielmo Riva was also with us. Later, Signor Stensen became my gracious host and friend."

But let us return with Stensen briefly to his anatomical studies, his dissections of the cadavers of animals and men. There was still much he felt he must discover, for, in his own words: "Beautiful is that which is seen, more beautiful is that which is

66

known, and a thousand times more beautiful is that which is unknown."

In a letter of October, 1666, Magalotti, a member of the Cimento Academy, wrote to his friend Segni, expressing admiration of certain of Stensen's experiments: "The other day by injecting various substances into the veins of a dog, he caused immediate death by coagulating the blood. He paralyzed the hind legs of another dog so that its forelegs dragged as though a heavy stone had been fastened to its tail. This result was obtained by a ligature of the descending aorta. Once this was removed, the dog walked as though nothing had happened."

It is impossible to describe all of Stensen's experiments. We will only mention those he made on the heart and vascular system of an eagle and a dog through which by means of injections, pressure, insufflation and heat, he established that heart action can be restored not only in the body of the heart but in all its fibers.

Scientia inflat, says an old adage. But this was not true in Stensen's case. He was modesty itself, and the careful and hesitating manner in which he presented his observations and discoveries was often remarked. He took no part in intrigues or dissensions. He wrote: "I made it a rule of life to perform each day that work which seemed most proper at the time, according to the place in which I found myself and within the limits of my capacities; to live without anxiety about the future; consequently to use no recommendations and bestow no gifts in order to obtain honors or employment, or in the hope of obtaining them. I often asked my relatives to solicit nothing on my behalf, intending to do what it was possible for me to do, and leaving the rest to God."

Such was Stensen as he indefatigably explored the byways of science.

V

The Great Decision

DURING THE YEARS 1666 and 1667, in the midst of his multifarious scientific activities, Niels Stensen was passing through a severe religious crisis.

He was an orthodox Lutheran, reared in a pious family which counted several Lutheran ministers among its members, but in his deep involvement in his study of the natural sciences, he had given little attention to religious matters. Some years earlier, as we have seen, when on his travels a Jesuit priest in Cologne had tried to turn his attention to questions of belief, he had refused to discuss the subject and had tried to change the conversation. He still felt that the Word of God was to be found whole and entire in the Scriptures and held to Luther's teaching regarding each individual's right to interpret them.

In Holland where, in contrast to strictly Lutheran Denmark, tolerance between kindred confessions prevailed on a rationalistic basis, Stensen had felt somewhat less secure in his original beliefs. For a brief time, as we have seen, he had been attracted to the Cartesian method of universal doubt.

In Paris he had encountered certain Catholics whose lives and conversation had impressed him, among them the Jesuit Jean de la Barre and Countess Helvig Rantzau whose words about the Eucharist, Stensen later said, he never forgot. His conversations, in 1665, with Bossuet had not changed his Lutheran convictions, and yet the arguments of the famous orator and Bishop of Meaux, to whom we owe among other writings the *History of the Variations of the Protestant Churches*, were grounded on long study of ecumenical problems and were expressed in most persuasive terms.

We might be surprised at Stensen's obstinacy—and it was he who accused himself of this—if we did not realize how difficult it is to change the beliefs one has accepted in childhood, heard taught by schoolmasters, and to which whole nations had adhered over a period of years. There were perhaps other motives for his resistance: an element of human respect, of self-esteem, the disinclination of a strong character to repudiate expressed opinions, an innate disposition to allow things to ripen of themselves without interposing one's own will "so as to make certain that it is only by God's will that whatever happens, comes at its proper time." Consequently he avoided discussions with the clergy and placed everything in the hands of God who, at an hour to be determined by Him, would enlighten his soul.

This pious abandonment to Providence is commendable if

69

it is accompanied by personal co-operation. However, when doubts had first assailed him, Stensen had remained passive and had not sought to clarify his mind regarding his religious views. Thus it is true, in a sense, as wrote Cosimo de' Medici, he had been drawn to the Catholic faith almost without knowing it.

During his first visit to Rome, in 1666, he was graciously received by Father Charles de Noyelle, at that time representative of the Germanic countries at the Jesuit curia. Later, in 1682, Father de Noyelle was elected General of the Society of Jesus, and in his letter of congratulation written at that time Stensen speaks with gratitude of their first meeting and adds that "undoubtedly His Paternity's prayers had been destined, in God's mercy, to aid in my conversion."

On June 24, 1666, shortly after his encounter with Father de Noyelle, Stensen was in Leghorn and witnessed a Corpus Christi procession which affected him profoundly. In a letter to a friend he wrote: "When I saw the Host carried amid such pomp across the city, the thought came into my mind: either this Host is a simple piece of bread and those who render It such honor are mad, or else It is truly the Body of Christ. In that case, why should I too not honor It? When this idea flashed across my mind, on one hand I could not persuade myself that so great a part of the Christian world was mad—thinking of the Roman Catholics, among whom there were so many intelligent and learned men—and on the other hand, I did not want to condemn the faith in which I was raised. Nevertheless, I had to decide between one and the other, because there was no way of reconciling the two opposing propositions nor to consider as true whichever religion was in error, and led its adherents into error, on a point so essential to the Christian faith.

"In this state of mind I went back to Florence to spend some

70

time studying the language spoken there in so pure a form, and then to continue my travels to other cities in Italy. In Florence, in order to do away with the uncertainty which troubled me on the subject of the mystery of the Eucharist, I spent much time in seeking the truth, trusting to God to open my soul to the knowledge I sought in all sincerity of heart, despite the fact the education I had received in the Lutheran faith made it difficult for me to forsake my old ideas."

This letter was addressed to Lavinia Arnolfini of whom Stensen was to say: "After God, I owe much of my conversion to this excellent lady."

Born at Lucca of a noble family, in 1631, Signora Arnolfini was the wife of Silvestro Arnolfini, ambassador of Lucca to the court of the Grand Duke of Tuscany. A woman of great piety, she practiced many austerities in secret, and at the same time graciously carried out the duties of her station in life. Niels Stensen was introduced to her by his friend Francesco Redi, and the high-minded Dane and the noble lady were soon on a basis of friendship and understanding. He was to call her "my mother in Christ" and never forgot, not even during the years of his later incessant and fatiguing labors in Northern Germany, the spiritual benefits he received through this pious friend. He was to write her often, although unfortunately only eight letters of this correspondence have come down to us.

Also through Redi, Stensen met another lady who was to give him great help and support during his spiritual travail. This was an elderly nun, Sister Maria Flavia del Nero, the daughter of Senator Alessandro of the barons of Porcigliano. Stensen was to visit her many times at the dispensary of the Annalena convent.

Sister Flavia del Nero was a most devout and charitable religious, at the same time a highly energetic and outspoken

71

woman. On their very first meeting she taxed Stensen on being "a heretic." He did not seem too much troubled by her forthright manner and took pleasure in his talks with her. She spoke to him of the supernatural with humble sincerity, told him directly what she thought, and did not hesitate to urge him to become a Catholic.

"May God open your eyes!" she said. "Pray to Him that you may come to know the truth. Promise me you will!"

Stensen made this promise, and beginning that day he recited each evening a prayer for this intention.

In his *Defensio epistolae de proprio conversione* he later wrote: "Very often it seemed difficult for me to change my will or my opinion; but I learned by repeated experience that I was delivered by this means (prayer) from many evils and was accorded a succession of favors. At such times I said the following prayer: 'Lord, without whose knowledge no hair falls from our head, no leaf from a tree, no bird from the air. . . . until now You have led me by ways unknown to me. Guide me still, whether I will it or not, along the paths of your grace. It is easier for You to guide me where You will than for me to renounce those things which I hold in my affections.' "

This may well have been the evening prayer he said each evening at Sister Flavia's request.

One day she asked him: "When will you come into the Church?"

"I am coming, I am coming," he replied. "But first I must learn everything about it. In the meanwhile, don't stop praying for me."

Usually on leaving her, he would ask the following favor: "Don't tell anyone of our conversations. No one must know I am taking an interest in things having to do with the Catholic religion."

72

Complex motives were at the basis of his hesitation. He wrote in the apologia from which we have already quoted: "During this time of my last hesitations, all the unfortunate things I had heard on the subject of converts to Catholicism came into my mind. It seemed to me I could not hope for any better treatment."

Flavia del Nero, considering herself unqualified to deal with theological problems, and believing the Dane in a favorable frame of mind, asked him to go to see a Barnabite priest, Father Leonelli. Niels went several times, but could not come to a decision, leaving the priest hurt and discouraged in his attempts to convince him. Several of his friends among the scientists also tried to persuade him, bringing up supernatural matters in the course of conversations regarding the natural sciences; they too began to lose hope.

We do not know whether Redi could still have written at this time what he said in the letter addressed to Valerio Inghirami immediately after Stensen's arrival in Florence: "I say again that Signor Niels Stensen should abandon Lutheranism and become a Catholic. I see so many signs in this direction that I can say this with assurance. May God be blessed and praised! Believe me, dear Signor Valerio, Signor Niels is really exemplary in his way of life; besides, he is a great philosopher, a great anatomist and a great mathematician."

Sister Flavia, after many months of fruitless conversations, tried to push Niels to make up his mind, saying that otherwise she thought it useless for him to continue his visits to her. He begged her to be patient, and in order not to abandon him, the nun called Signora Arnolfini to her aid.

The ambassador's wife confessed that she too felt discouraged, but was continuing her prayers for Stensen's conversion. She had decided, she said, to have him meet her confessor, Fa-

73

ther Aemilius Savignani, the learned Jesuit who was rector of the college of the Society in Florence.

When next Stensen went to see Signora Arnolfini in her splendid palace on the Via de' Bardi, she deftly turned the conversation to the spiritual theme, and begged him with tears in her eyes to try to understand the importance of the Catholic faith. This time Stensen promised her to apply himself seriously to the study of religion, and he made good this promise.

He tells us: "Not only did I talk of these questions with learned men of whom there were many among the Catholics, but I also tried to find as much light as I could with the help of Holy Scripture and the most ancient Christian writings."

He went frequently to see Father Savignani, told him of his doubts, asked for explanations, and tried to rid himself of his objections to the Church's teachings on such points as the sacraments, purgatory, the authority of the Pope. Hour after hour he was to be found in the library of San Lorenzo, bending over old Greek and Hebrew manuscripts, comparing the Latin version of the Bible, which he did not trust entirely, with the original texts.

Study and prayer all helped to give him moral certainty, but grace, the decisive factor, was still lacking. Then on November 2, 1667, as he was on his way from the Arnolfini palace to the Jesuit college in Florence, he suddenly dropped certain doubts and troubles of mind which had continued to linger, and put aside his misgivings.

On reaching the Jesuit residence, at that time on the Via Borgio Pinto, he climbed the stairs to the room of Father Savignani and casting himself on his knees before the priest, said: "At last it is decided! I wish to become a Catholic."

Much moved, Father Savignani raised him to his feet, saying: "God be praised! God be praised!" Going to the chapel,

74

they joined in thanksgiving for the grace of Stensen's conversion.

After the two had discussed what must be done on the day following, Stensen went to give the glad tidings to the two ladies who had been of such edification and help to him— Signora Lavinia Arnolfini and Sister Maria Flavia del Nero. As the good Sister wrote later: "The next morning, November 3, Signor Stensen requested some relics and a picture of the Annunciation which I had promised to give him when he became a Catholic. He also sent me 50 *scudi* (about fifty dollars) to defray the cost of a pair of silver candelabra to be placed before the statue of the Virgin we have in our oratory. The Sisters of our community had often prayed to Our Lady for his intentions before this statue."

That same day, together with Father Savignani, Niels Stensen went to the Holy Office in Florence and signed a formal petition to be received into the Catholic Church. On November 7, still in the company of Father Savignani, he abjured his former Lutheranism and made the prescribed confession of faith before the Inquisitor Girolamo di Lugo, a member of the Franciscan order.

The news of Stensen's conversion soon spread throughout the city and even beyond the frontiers of Tuscany. In the Florence of that day all eyes were on the Pitti Palace, and everything that pertained to the grand duke, his family or the members of his court was of the greatest interest. To the Florentines of all ranks and classes Stensen had become a familiar and highly respected figure.

In a letter dated November 29, the papal nuncio, Lorenzo Trotti, informed the Cardinal Secretary of State in Rome of the Danish scientist's conversion, telling him of the part taken in it by the Jesuit Fathers. He also stated that as a demonstra-

75

tion of his allegiance to the Roman Pontiff, the new convert wished to receive Confirmation from the hands of the papal representative in Florence. The reply transmitted the Pope's message that the Danish gentleman's conversion had given him great consolation, and carried his felicitations to the Jesuit Father and to the apostolic nuncio in Tuscany.

Stensen now devoted himself to his spiritual life, and proved himself worthy of the praise bestowed on him ten years later by Francesco Nerli, the archbishop of Florence.

"While still outside the Church, he lived an upright life and had acquired many moral virtues. On becoming a Catholic he prescribed for himself a rigorous discipline, and observed it so faithfully that he soon acquired a high degree of Christian perfection. He became known as a man of deep piety, and one in continual union with God. He was forgetful of self and filled with charity toward his neighbor, visiting the sick in the hospitals and prisoners in their cells, and taking care of their spiritual and corporal needs.

"His zeal for the glory of God and the salvation of souls led him to seek occasions to win the friendship of Jews and non-Catholic Christians who came to Florence on business or for other reasons. Because of his gentle manners and the effectiveness of his gift of persuasion, which was truly astonishing, he succeeded in converting certain among them, and since generally these converts on entering the Catholic Church severed their former ties, Stensen with the help of the grand duke provided them with other means of earning a livelihood.

"All these activities won for him the esteem of all, without in any way affecting the poor opinion he had of himself. Although he was considered by those competent to judge as the best anatomist in Italy, a master of other knowledge, and expert in various languages, those who saw him most frequently were never to see him make any display of superiority. . . . His letters to his friends have the charm of great simplicity and Christian humility."

We know that Stensen's first confessor was none other than his Jesuit friend, Father Savignani. We know, too, that beside his fellow-scientists of the Cimento Academy, he counted as friends many learned ecclesiastics. Stensen continued to carry on his scientific experiments and his duties at the Pitti Palace; nevertheless, he spent much time in the churches in prayer before the Blessed Sacrament.

On the feast of the Immaculate Conception, December 8, 1667, Stensen renewed his profession of faith before the apostolic nuncio Lorenzo Trotti. That very day there came to him a surprising summons.

In a letter written by Vincenzo Viviani to Lorenzo Magalotti, a fellow member of the Cimento Academy at that time away from Florence, we read: "The honorable Signor Stensen selected All Souls' Day to declare himself a Catholic. He has already gone through all the formalities, to the great joy of their Serene Highnesses, and of all his friends. Then, on the feast of the Immaculate Conception, after he had renewed his profession of faith before the Apostolic Nuncio, he received from his King (Frederick III) a summons enjoining him to return immediately to Denmark and guaranteeing him an annual stipend of 400 thalers (at that time around four thousand dollars), together with a promise of more important advancement later."

Stensen's response to the summons of the king of Denmark was a formal petition for personal religious liberty.

VI

Travels and Controversy

WHILE WAITING for King Frederick's reply to his petition, Stensen divided his time during the months following his entrance into the Catholic Church between theological and scientific studies. In the spring of 1668 he made field trips to Volterra and the surrounding Tuscan country, gathering specimens and working on an explicit systematic survey of his geological findings. He also went to Pisa with the Court and was, it seems, much occupied for we have only a few letters written by him at this period.

Volterra was an ancient Etruscan city, antedating Rome. In

the remains of its oldest walls and in the stones of its forum, Stensen was able to find and study striated shells of every kind, and in the city's environs to observe many interesting geological phenomena—petrefacts, hot springs and other signs of ancient volcanism. He was working at this time on a report of his geological researches, a preliminary to a longer treatise he intended to write. This 78-page report, *De Solido intra solidum naturaliter contento dissertationis prodromus*,[1] usually called the *Prodromus* or *De Solido*, is considered one of the most valuable publications in the history of science, for it indicates a new line of scientific thought and established Stensen as the founder of scientific geology and mineralogy (crystallography).

In the *Prodromus*, Stensen demonstrates certain theses showing that solid bodies (shells, fossils, etc.) have their origin and growth in a fluid; that two bodies in all respects similar are produced by the same process; that of two contiguous bodies the first one to harden has given its form to the other. He concludes that from the nature of the body and the place where it is found, it is possible to determine with some degree of certainty its origin and process of formation; he applies this notion to bodies enclosed in other bodies.

He then passes to an examination of the structure of certain particular bodies, indicating in each case what can be said positively regarding its substance and the place and manner in which it was produced. He attributes to deposits of liquid the superimposed strata of the earth and the different compositions of the strata. He notes that each of these could only have been

---

[1] The *Prodromus* was translated into English in Stensen's lifetime (as early as 1671). A modern English version with an introduction and explanatory notes by John Garrett Winter was published in 1916 (University of Michigan Studies—Humanistic Series, vol. XI) under the title *The Prodromus of Nicolaus Steno's Dissertation Concerning a Solid Body Enclosed by Process of Nature Within a Solid.—Trans.*

formed by the mixture of their substance with a liquid and if it were deposited in place by its own weight and afterward leveled by the movement of the liquid flowing over it.

He also states that at a time when any given stratum was formed, with the exception of the lowest, its upper surface was parallel to the horizon. "All strata, therefore, except the lowest, are bounded by two planes parallel to the horizon." From this he concludes that perpendicular or curved strata seen today were at one time horizontal. He attributes their changed position to violent movements caused by volcanoes.

"For just as water, disintegrating earthy material, carries it down sloping places, not only on the surface of the earth but also in the earth's cavities, so fire, breaking up whatever solids oppose it, not only drives out their lighter particles, but sometimes hurls forth their heaviest weights, and the result is that on the surface of the earth are formed steeps, channels and hollows, while in the bowels of the earth subterranean passages and caverns are produced. And by reason of the diversity of the cavities and cracks the broken strata assume different positions, while some remain parallel to the horizon, others become perpendicular to it, many form oblique angles with it, and not a few are twisted into curves because their substance is tenacious."

This leads to the problem of the origin of mountains. "Alteration in the position of strata is the chief cause of the mountain formation which may be seen in any given range of mountains." But mountains may also be formed in other ways "as by the eruption of fires which belch forth ashes and stones together with sulphur and bitumen, and also by the violence of rain torrents, whereby the stony strata, which have already become rent apart by the alternation of heat and cold are tumbled headlong; while the earthy strata, forming cracks under great blasts of heat, are broken up into various parts."

In connection with the formation of mountains Stensen discusses the origin of ores and mineral crystals. Regarding his comments on the form, growth and shapes of crystals, Professor A. Casati, in an address delivered at the opening of a congress of radiologists on the island of Elba in September, 1951, had this to say of Stensen:

"It was during his studies of the minerals of this island that Stensen, the anatomist of the salivary duct, a Dane by birth but a Florentine by predilection, saw, understood and described the importance and beauty of crystal, nature's marvelous work of art, in which by the phenomenon of crystallization, an almost vital process of the inorganic world, matter is fixed and repeated in definite and characteristic shapes through the pressure of constant and immutable forces. Stensen wrote of the law of constancy of interfacial angles and recognized its causes. In this he was the precursor of Haüy, the founder of crystallography."

With regard to shells and mollusks, Stensen says in the *Prodromus* it is sufficient to examine these bodies to demonstrate that they belonged to animals that lived in liquid. He also discusses other zoological remains found in the earth such as teeth, skulls and other bones.

Finally, he gives an outline of the geological evolution of Tuscany. In six drawings he illustrates this evolution showing that it was twice covered by water, was twice a dry plain, and twice dislocated by volcanic eruptions which formed mountains.

It was his observation that this evolution had not been confined to Tuscany, but that similar changes had taken place all

81

over the earth. Like many another great scientist, he was happy to affirm that there is "conformity and consent . . . between nature and Holy Scripture."

Stensen was in his thirty-first year when he delivered the *Prodromus* to Viviani who saw to its publication (in 1669). This was his last geological treatise.

In the summer of 1668, Stensen appears to have received a favorable reply from Denmark to his request for personal religious liberty. Apparently he was still engrossed in his geological researches and would have preferred to remain in Italy and write the continuation of the *De Solido*. At any rate he made ready his departure from Florence, but took a roundabout route to his northern homeland. On this journey he planned not only to visit new sites in order to further his researches but to try to win his friends to the Catholic faith.

Having provided himself with letters of introduction, he set out that autumn for Rome which at that time was under the short pontificate of Clement IX (Giulio Rospigliosi, a Tuscan). Through the good offices of Cardinal Leopoldo de' Medici, Stensen gained access to certain books in the Vatican Library that were not then available to the general public. He also discussed various scientific problems with the mathematician and later Cardinal Michelangelo Ricci.

From the city on the Tiber Stensen went farther south, to the Kingdom of Naples and Sicily. The pestilence which had started in Naples in 1656 had led to much desolation and disorder; and, in late 1668, the roads continued to be infested with bandits. Stensen's friends in Rome tried to dissuade him from undertaking this journey so fraught with danger. Their efforts were in vain, for to him Vesuvius held an irresistible attraction.

It is likely that this visit to Naples also included Sicily and

Malta, but at Christmas he was back in Rome, and during the first weeks of the new year (1669) he traversed the Apennines. He was in Bologna on February 9, enjoying the company of his friend Marcello Malpighi with whom he discussed many scientific questions, especially the question of muscle structure and embryological experiments.

Some three weeks later he set foot in the Republic of Venice. Although this was not a happy time for the once mighty Queen of the Adriatic (the Turks took Crete from her in 1669), Stensen contracted a familiar acquaintance with men of learning in the city of Venice and Murano. Among these was Carlo Fracassati, a professor of anatomy, and Geminiano Montanari, well known for his studies in blood transfusions.

On April 20th Stensen wrote from Venice to his friend Viviani that he was still waiting for a letter from King Frederick which he had been informed was on its way from Denmark. But the letter never arrived, and Stensen continued his travels. His next stop was at Innsbruck. In a letter dated May 12, 1669, the Danish scientist thanked the Tuscan Grand Duke Ferdinand for the cordial reception given him by his sister, Anna de' Medici, the consort of the governor of the Austrian Tyrol. At the same time the Medici lady wrote a glowing letter to her brother in Tuscany, expressing her appreciation for the opportunity of making the acquaintance of so erudite and virtuous a man as Stensen. In it she recounts the scholarly lecture that the Dane had given in Innsbruck after his visit to the ore mines of Schwaz and the salt pits of Halle, and his excursion to the emerald fields in Habachtal in the Salzburg district. She also describes Stensen's dissection of the head of a monstrous calf "which could not raise its head because in place of his brain there were four pounds of water."

In June, Stensen was in Nuremberg, a city in the Franconian

area of Bavaria. Here he made the acquaintance of Johann Georg Volckamer the Elder, a physician and naturalist. After geological and mineralogical studies in the eroded terrace lands of Franconia, he went to Vienna, probably by way of the Danube River, and here we find him at the end of July, 1669, continuing his journey in the late summer to Hungary, above all in order to examine the gold and silver mines in Schemnitz and Kremnitz and the southwestern part of the Slovakian ore mines.

Stensen spent two full months in Hungary. On October 12th he was back again in Vienna. In a letter addressed to Marcello Malpighi at Bologna, he wrote: "I had hoped to bring my pilgrimage to a close this autumn, but I am not much further advanced in my studies than when I visited you. It would take very little for me to abandon my return to Denmark."

This letter is followed by six months of silence. Then, from a letter dated April 20, 1670, we learn that he was then stopping in Amsterdam, Holland.

On this journey Stensen did not reach his native land. The death of King Frederick III in February 1670, had altered the situation and left the Dane free to continue his own work. From Amsterdam, Stensen moved to Utrecht, from whence he wrote to Cardinal Leopoldo de' Medici: "In Amsterdam I passed several months in the company of M. Thévenot."

In the first days of June he hurriedly departed for Florence upon receiving news of the grave illness of his patron and friend, Grand Duke Ferdinand. Despite all haste, he arrived too late. Ferdinand's remains were already entombed in a new sacristy of the Church of San Lorenzo, and his son Cosimo III (1642–1723) was now grand duke of Tuscany.

On his return to Florence one of Stensen's first preoccupations was to write to Johannes Sylvius, a minister of the German Reformed Church in Amsterdam, whose conversion he hoped to bring about. During his visit to Holland he had taken part in many lively discussions with his old friends concerning the interpretation of Holy Writ and the matter of ecclesiastical authority. These friends had arranged his meeting with Sylvius.

Stensen had several conversations with this clergyman before his departure from Holland, and in the course of their last interview had thought he had brought him to a decision. In the letter to which we refer, he addressed him in the most friendly terms: "I write you with all the more pleasure because I have experienced your moderation in discussion; I therefore foster all the more hope that the examination of so serious and important a question, which we both undertook for the highest motives, will be brought to a happy conclusion."

He ended by recalling an objection Sylvius had raised in the course of their last meeting. Stensen replied: "We do not say that the Catholic Church is the true Church of God for the reason that these are God's words, but because the marks of the true Church as defined by God correspond to the marks of the Roman Church today; these marks are self-evident and confirmed by the facts of history down through the centuries."

Sylvius proved to be less than civil in his reply. He began by denouncing Stensen's zeal for the Roman Church as blind and irresponsible, calling him "an ingenuous disputant," "irresponsible," and one with whom "it was time lost to engage in disputation." He then went on: "I am petrified to see that you, an erudite man, put in doubt the religion in which you were born; that you are so credulous as to embrace the Roman religion; that you have vowed blind obedience to this Church, to the point of considering divine those incoherent things that are proposed by the Church of Rome."

Sylvius then set out to compare certain precepts of the Catholic Church with certain counsels of Sacred Scripture, claiming that the two did not concur. He then asked if it was possible that the content of the Roman faith was actually to be found in Holy Scripture. He concludes by stating that Holy Writ is the only rule and law of faith and morals.

An "ingenuous disputant"! What an affront to Stensen; but this was nothing new. Ever since his conversion to the Catholic faith he had been subjected to similar name-calling by former friends and associates.

The result of this exchange of letters was a new endeavor on Stensen's part—theological writings. The first of these was the *Examen objectionis circa diversas scripturas sacras et earum interpretationes* completed at Florence and dispatched to Sylvius on July 15, 1670. In this he underlined the point that there is no revealed doctrine proclaimed by the Church which is not contained in its exact substance in the sources of Revelation, that is, Scripture and Tradition. However, he said, it is not always expressly revealed in specific words and is often contained wrapped in other truths. It is therefore the function of the Church to clarify and interpret authoritatively what is said.

In another epistle written at this time Stensen attacks the confusion caused by rationalistic interpretation of the Bible, a result of the principle of the right of private judgment in scriptural matters. He was still trying to convince Sylvius and at the same time to reach through him to other of his Dutch friends, both Lutheran and Calvinist. In his *De propria conversione epistola* he gives the reasons which led him from orthodox Lutheranism to the Catholic Church. His *Ad novae philosophiae* showed that he wished to make himself understood not only by the Dutch Calvinists, but that he also bore in mind the rationalistic and pantheistic views of Spinoza and the flaws of the Cartesian philosophy as formulated by the latter.

86

Stensen's debate with his Dutch friends, especially Johannes Sylvius, was carried on for some time after his return to Florence. His theological writings were first circulated in manuscript among his correspondents, and most of them were not published until some years later, after his ordination to the priesthood and his consecration as a bishop. From one of his tracts, *Occasio sermonum de religione cum Joanne Silvio*, published in Hanover in 1678, we will quote a few pages in order for the reader to form an idea of Stensen's method of controversy:

"When, after receiving from God the favor of my conversion, I spent several months in Amsterdam, my Calvinist friends professed great pity for me for having been persuaded by Catholics into obedience to the Church. According to them, the Church rests solely on the authority of men, and abounds in dogmatic errors and scandals.

"Among her erroneous doctrines they mentioned idolatry, an exaggerated reliance on good works as a means to salvation, and immunity granted by ecclesiastics to the worst of criminals as well as other kinds of evil-doers.

"They said that the certitude of our faith rests upon men, even upon one man; in this way the Word of God is ignored and is replaced by doctrines taught by men.

"When I heard my friends say such things, although I was touched by their solicitude for my salvation, I was pained to see souls athirst for truth departing from that same truth by arguments which would do nothing to convince Catholics they were in error but which would only arouse hatred among ignorant people.

"The Protestant aversion toward us has two causes. The first extends to all Catholics and is based on the erroneous idea spread among their followers by the leaders of the revolt against the Church that men's misdeeds, whether they spring from malice or from ignorance, are to be attributed to the doctrines they accept. The second cause is the damage inflicted by Catholics during the Flemish war; those who suffered at that time are unable to forget their hatred for those who inflicted it.

"The pain caused me by the unhappy state of my friends was increased by my awareness of my own human frailty. I recalled the time and effort it had taken me to surmount even one of the above prejudices, and I could easily imagine how much more difficult it would have been if both were present.

"Consequently, I would like again to set forth the truth that the errors of some should not be attributed to all; that men's vices are not to be laid to the door of a doctrine that expressly condemns those vices. I have shown that there is nothing in Catholic doctrine that could make it suspect of idolatry, since it teaches that one should adore God alone and that although those who carried out the divine will should be venerated, they should never be granted the worship rendered to the Almighty. In the same way there is nothing in the Church's teaching regarding good works that could be accused of presumption, since the origin, performance and perfection of such works stem entirely from the grace given by Christ.

"As regards the immunity extended by ecclesiastics to malefactors who seek sanctuary in holy places, I replied that this clemency was granted for reasons of justice and prudence; if it is not in accord with human prudence, it is not the fault of the doctrine.

"We close our eyes to many things, but that is not to say we approve them; it only shows the difficulties that exist in dealing with them, and the fear that in extirpating a lesser scandal the way is paved for a greater one. Let all those who proclaim themselves Christian in name show themselves Christian in their deeds. As for those who call themselves Christians yet live a life worse than pagan, such men can be converted by God alone; they can be expelled from Christian society only by giving scandal to the weak. Let us think of the cockle which God allows to grow with the wheat and which he forbids reaping until the harvest, so that the good grain may not be destroyed with the chaff. . . .

"Finally to say that our doctrine teaches vice of any kind, or in any way sanctions it, is entirely contrary to fact. The Church at all times condemns vice publicly in writings and sermons, but also it rescues many sinners and brings them back to God. In every great city I have seen the same vices, but not the same virtues. Do not rail against the vice found in Italian cities when the same vices infect the cities of Holland. . . .

"If vices in every place resemble one another, the same cannot be said of the virtues. The difference is noteworthy, as is shown in the lives of Catholic confessors, martyrs, virgins, celibates, missionaries, and other men and women in every walk of life."

Stensen then devotes several pages to other objections which arose in the controversy with Sylvius and his friends. In this connection he remarks: "In such discussions, it is difficult to bring the truth fully to the light because the subject is too often changed and there are many digressions. The line of reasoning is not only interrupted but almost always cut short, so that no one of the controversial questions is really solved."

Despite all his zeal, Stensen had no success in convincing Sylvius who remained unshaken in his Calvinism. The Dane did not give up easily and, as we have seen, continued this correspondence for some length of time. Despite Sylvius' broadsides against him, he continued to pray for him in Christian charity, "so that before his death Divine mercy would be granted him to recognize—before it is too late—the spiritual benefits he could obtain for himself and for others."

VII

From Light to Light

WITH THE DEATH of Ferdinand II in May, 1670, Stensen had lost a generous patron, but he acquired another in his son and successor, Cosimo III (1642–1723). The attitude of the grand duke toward the Dane was that of a friend to a friend rather than of a ruler to his courtier, and this relationship was to continue uninterrupted as long as Stensen lived. Following in his father's footsteps, the new grand duke accorded Stensen every honor, provided him with comfortable lodgings, a subsidy, and the most favorable conditions for research and study.

Despite Cosimo's unfavorable treatment by various historians, he was not the monster he has been painted by some. Stensen remained for a long time in his service, and always spoke and wrote of him in the highest terms. One might think he thus put himself on record out of gratitude, but one of Stensen's scrupulous sincerity would scarcely have distorted the truth from motives of self-interest.

For one thing, it is impossible not to admire the patience with which Cosimo supported the scourge of his unhappy marriage to Marguerite d'Orléans, who made all sorts of scenes and dishonored him in public. It was only upon the insistence of others that he finally consented to allow her to return with a brilliant escort to Paris, to live in retirement in a convent of Montmartre. In this "retirement" she continued her extravagances and the worldly life to which she was accustomed and indulged in even more outrageous behavior. Such was the woman whom certain historians, reversing the roles, pity for her marriage to the diabolical tyrant, Cosimo!

The grand duke was much interested in the Dane's geological work and was particularly anxious that the planned treatise, to which the *Prodromus* was a forerunner, be completed. Nevertheless, he accorded Stensen time for the theological studies the latter felt he must undertake in order to carry on his debate with Sylvius. Stensen was also preparing himself as the tutor of Cosimo's son in moral and philosophical subjects as well as in natural science, a position that had been offered him on his return to Florence.

Thus from the autumn of 1670 to the spring of 1671, we find him at his desk in the Medici palace near San Marco, deep in the great tomes lent him by his friends among the clergy. He was trying to provide himself with the weapons he needed to combat heresy and to bring back to the Church those who had

91

strayed. Perhaps within his heart, he had already heard the first whisperings of a call to the priesthood.

In the spring of 1671 he had completed the task he had assigned himself and returned to his work in geology and mineralogy. That summer he undertook a journey to the sub-Alpine region of Lombardy. There he made a study of the Moncodino grotto by the Lake of Como and the Gresta grotto by the Lake of Gardo in order to disprove the Aristotelian theory of *antiperistasis*, or "the battle between cold and heat." (This theory was said to explain such conditions as the cold within an underground cave or the hot lava within a snow-covered volcano.)

The Cimento academicians were then much interested in the antiperistasis theory, but seriously questioned it. That it was erroneous was confirmed by Stensen's investigation of the grottos. In two letters addressed to the grand duke, Stensen stated that there is no antiperistasis: the ice in the caves was not due to the cold concentrated within them by the heat without.

Unfortunately Stensen never seemed to be able to stay long in one place. On December 23, 1671, he received a letter from Copenhagen in which he was notified that his king, Christian V of Denmark, intended to recall him to a post as professor of anatomy in his native city, and asking if he would accept the invitation.

Stensen was undecided. On one hand, he did not wish to displease his sovereign, to miss this opportunity to see his family, nor to refuse the occasion to carry his faith to his compatriots, an apostolate now made easier by the fact that religious liberty had been proclaimed in Denmark on November 16, 1670. On the other hand, he felt bound to Florence by ties of gratitude, friendship and the interests of his work. He wrote at once to Cosimo asking for his directive and advice. The grand duke replied that "he would leave him at liberty to decide," and added: "I can only assure you that I will always be glad to see you, and that you will retain the same favor and affection I have always extended to you. I do not doubt that wherever you go, God will use your talents and exemplary virtues for the good of others, and perhaps make them even more fruitful in a country that has been lost to our faith."

Stensen accepted, and in February 1672 received the official letter of appointment from King Christian. He left his beloved Florence in May, to the sorrow of his friends. In a letter written by Lorenzo Magalotti we read: "The liberty of conscience granted in his country redounds to our loss. Stensen has been recalled by his king, and promised an annual stipend of 400 thalers. However, I believe that he will return here for the Holy Year (1675)."

Niels, in fact, had written to Grand Duke Cosimo: "I do not lose hope that my King will permit me to come back to serve Your Highness after several years."

In his letter mentioned above, Magalotti went on: "His departure irritates me, for besides losing a friend—and I might almost say a spiritual father—I am now saddled with the burdensome task of superintending the museum of natural history."

Before starting on his homeward travels Stensen had undertaken a last service for his Medici friend and patron, Cosimo III. He arranged and made an inventory of the whole collection of natural products at the University of Pisa. Many of the specimens were donated by Stensen himself, nor was this the first time that the Danish scientist contributed to the Medici famous paleontological-geological-mineralogical collection.

Prior to his first departure from Tuscany, Stensen donated the entire fine collection of minerals, crystals and various fossils which he had acquired in his travels in the Italian Peninsula and the island of Elba before he wrote the *De Solido*. This collection had been catalogued by Stensen himself and housed in the natural history museum of the Pitti Palace in Florence. After Ferdinand's death his son and grandson added more specimens. These came by way of gifts from travelers and missionaries; also from the Elector of Saxony who sent minerals and ores; from the Spanish court which sent a valuable collection of gold and silver ores and emeralds from its overseas possessions of Chile and Peru. Then, too, from the coasts of Africa and Asia came the crustacea.

The manuscript of Stensen's inventory describing the objects stored at Pisa and the Pitti Palace in Florence has been lost. Fortunately, when, in 1763, Giovanni Targioni Tozzetti made a compilation of the by then much augmented Tuscan collection, he included Stensen's inventory. This compilation is divided into three sections: (1) animals and their parts; (2) plants; (3) fossils and minerals; also the *Indice di Cose Naturali* (Index of Natural Things)—an inventory of Stensen's specimens which consists of items of value from his researches in the late 1660's and early 1670's.

On an uncomfortable journey northward by horseback and coach, Stensen stopped in Bologna to see his friend Marcello Malpighi, who discussed his latest observations with him. After another stop in Innsbruck, he went on to Dresden in the company of a certain Gabriel Angelo Battistini, who introduced him to the Elector of Saxony. It was on this occasion that the elector promised Stensen, who always kept in mind the Tuscan grand duke's geological interests, to add to the collection of the museum of natural history in Florence various stones and geological specimens found in his domains.

94

On July 3, 1672, Stensen was back in Copenhagen, a guest in his sister's house. Anna had married the goldsmith Jakob Kitzerow who had taken over the family workshop. Here no one importuned him on the subject of his change of religion; each considered that every one could be saved through his own, provided he led a good life. "I enjoy the same liberty as when I was in a Catholic country," he wrote, "and I live, as in Florence, between the church and my study."

From the correspondence with his Italian friends we learn that Stensen and the handful of Catholics then living in the Danish capital attended Mass and other liturgical services in a provisional chapel in the official residence of the French ambassador. Mention is also made of "some Lutherans" attending these religious services. The chaplain was a Jesuit priest, Johann Sterck, who became Stensen's confessor. The French ambassador had obtained permission to house four more priests and to build a chapel with a belfry alongside his official residence, but because of lack of funds the project was abandoned.

Stensen was appalled by the religious indifference daily manifested in the circles in which he moved. He deplored the spiritual state of his countrymen who "are outside the true Church and live in an illusion of profound security." In a letter to Cardinal Leopoldo de' Medici, he writes: "I can only feel compassion for them; especially as in this there is no real malice on their part, as one can see in the careful way they deal with matters other than religion. So far as religion is concerned, my way of talking about it appears to them altogether uncivilized."

In letter after letter we find this same lament: the cry of his soul for the sanctification of those with whom he came into contact. He wrote to Grand Duke Cosimo: "I beg Your Highness' prayers for these souls, and that some of your monthly alms be offered God to implore His mercy on this country, so

95

that His love may enter the hearts of men and His name be glorified with the same desire for spiritual perfection that I came to know in Italy."

Besides this spiritual torment, there were other disillusions. The annual stipend of 400 thalers which had been promised Stensen did not materialize for some time; nor did he receive accommodations wherein he could have enjoyed a measure of privacy and independence.

For several months he threw himself into anatomical demonstrations before his students (the Danish law against the dissection of human cadavers having been abrogated). Then came the directive that henceforth dissections would be made publicly in the national anatomical theater in Copenhagen.

On October 15, 1672, Stensen wrote to Opizio Pallavicini, apostolic nuncio to Tuscany: "I have unexpectedly been invited to dissect a human cadaver in public. I believe that God has permitted this either to accustom me to public speaking or else to prove to me by experience that I am not fitted for such exhibitions. I betray grave faults at such times. For one thing I have allowed my oral Latin to become rusty because I have been speaking modern languages. . . . It disturbs me to appear in public so unprepared. How much more the thought of appearing before the eyes of my true and only Judge disturbs me!"

Always the thought of God was uppermost in his mind. Here are the opening words of a lecture delivered at the University of Copenhagen (published in the third volume of the Danish periodical *Acta medica*): "My appearance before you, my honorable auditors from many countries, is due to the Author of the created works I shall show you, and to the liberality of a King to his subject. For these reasons I bespeak your attention. God has allowed me to make certain anatomical discoveries, even when I was not seeking them—discoveries not previously made by others more worthy than myself. It has pleased the King to reopen today the national anatomical theater, closed for many years, so that I might explain the experiments of others as well as my own. Please do not focus your attention on the wording or gestures of the demonstrator, but regard God's marvels as manifested in His works." He further explained that for those who engaged in them anatomical demonstrations should not be regarded with horror or sadness but as a way of recognizing and making known the Author of all nature.

Following this first appearance before the public, Stensen gave other demonstrations in addition to his work with his classes. His best known and most important public dissection took place in February, 1673, and was introduced by a *prooemium*, or preface, in which the anatomist described his purpose to be to guide his audience on to the three levels of natural science, the science of the mind, and faith. From this *prooemium* comes Stensen's often-quoted sentence: *"Pulchra quae videntur, pulchriora quae sciuntur, longe pulcherrima quae ignorantur"* (Beautiful is that which is seen, more beautiful is that which is known, and a thousand times more beautiful is that which is unknown).

Two of his university lectures given at this period are entitled the "Miscellaneous Questions Proposed by Niels Stensen" and "The Description of an Eagle's Muscles." The former shows Stensen to have been a stimulating teacher; the latter a keen researcher planning and working on a comparative study of the anatomy of animals. He also made contributions to two Danish scientific periodicals: the *Acta medica* and the *Philosophica Hafniensia*.

We will give no further details of his work in Copenhagen, nor describe his dissections of human and animal cadavers which have come down to us in the notes of one of his most enthusiastic pupils, Holger Jacobsen (known also by his Latin name, Oligerus Jacobeus). On the other hand, it is of interest to know why he again decided to leave his native country.

Despite the wide range of his scientific work, Stensen had no professional status on the academic level. A full professorship at the university was excluded, as adherence to the Lutheran state religion was required. It also seems that he soon clashed with Lutheran theologians and representatives of the state Church, and limits were set on his activities.

We have already seen that he was disappointed by delays in the payment of the stipend promised him and in the matter of his living arrangements. In a letter to Cardinal Leopoldo de' Medici, we read: "I will not speak of material matters, for God has given me a sister with whom I can live, and the financial condition of the Kingdom is such that all cannot be satisfied. . . . Certain people pity me when they see I am in the same situation as on the day of my arrival; however, to tell the truth, I am not so worried as they suppose."

Later on he was paid the amount that had been promised, but he still felt out of his element. Religious differences were uppermost in his thoughts and despite the tact of his friends and acquaintances, he confessed: "Here I am a barbarian; I am not understood."

Indeed he was not happy, and again Florence beckoned him with insistence. He thought of that city's innumerable churches, of the spiritual direction available from her priests, of the friends he had left there—Father Savignani, the Grand Duke Cosimo, the outspoken Flavia del Nero and the devout Lavinia Arnolfini —as well as the intellectual stimulation he derived from its circle of learned men.

When after a year he had been invited to make no further

98

public appearance in the anatomical theater, and felt further circumscribed in his work, he decided to return to the banks of the Arno. Addressing himself to Count Peter Griffenfeld, who held a position of trust and influence at the Danish court, he asked that King Christian V grant him permission to accept a post he had been offered as a tutor to the son of the Grand Duke of Tuscany.

He worded his letter under date of June 5, 1674, in the most tactful and diplomatic terms: "When Your Excellency communicated to me the King's order that I return to Copenhagen, the Grand Duke had already made known to me his desire that I undertake the task of tutoring his son and heir in natural philosophy. I promised that one day I would return to Italy and accept this position, provided that my King would grant me such permission. Since His Highness the Grand Duke now writes to me renewing his invitation, subject to His Majesty's approval, may I beg you to intercede with His Majesty that I be granted this permission." Continuing his letter, Stensen promised that once back in Italy, he would make every effort to increase commercial and cultural relations between Denmark and the Grand Duchy of Tuscany and ended by requesting a passport.

This passport, signed by the king, bears the date of July 14, 1674—one month and nine days later. Funds for the trip were provided by the Tuscan grand duke and a further sum in the amount of 300 thalers awaited him in the commercial city of Hamburg.

Writing from this North German city on August 11, 1674, Stensen informed Grand Duke Cosimo that his traveling companions were two converts on their way to Hildesheim and Cologne, and that he was also accompanied by a nephew, the son of his sister, Anna. He expressed the hope that the grand duke would admit this nephew, a medical student, to the staff of the hospital of Santa Maria Nuova.

The following day he left Hamburg and proceeded to the city of Hanover in the principality of Calenberg where he stayed for a fortnight as a guest of Duke Johann Friedrich of the house of Braunschweig-Lüneburg. The German prince and the Danish scientist had met in Copenhagen during the former's visit to his sister, the Danish Queen, Sophie Amalie. Duke Johann Friedrich, like Stensen, was a convert to the Catholic faith. This conversion had come about as a result of a visit to Italy, and through the friendship of Giuseppe da Cupertino (1603–1663), who was subsequently canonized by Pope Clement XIII.

The German prince invited Stensen three times to dine, thereby giving him the opportunity to speak with several Protestants on religious matters in an effort to win them to Catholicism. He also asked him to perform a heart dissection to demonstrate the functions of that organ. As a parting gift, the duke presented Stensen with a gold medallion bearing his portrait and a handsome sum of money with which to purchase a gold chain so that he could wear the medallion around his neck.

But Niels never wore the medallion. It would have been too pompous for his simple tastes. He therefore gave the money to a Capuchin friar, instructing him to return it to the duke after his departure from Hanover. With his customary delicacy, he found the excuse of banditry on the roads due to the unsettled conditions of the time (the Dutch-French war which had begun in 1672).

His travels southward, however, were without untoward incident. He made some conversions on this journey and in several places was able to extend help to new converts to Catholicism.

What was the date of his return to Florence? On December 2, 1674, Redi wrote to a friend expressing his delight that Stensen was about to arrive; from which it is deduced that he reached the city on the Arno either late in December, 1674, or during the first days of January, 1675.

In the middle of January began his appointment as one of a carefully selected group of tutors of the future grand duke of Tuscany. Stensen's task consisted in teaching young Ferdinand III (1663–1713) "Christian philosophy" which comprised natural science and metaphysics, as well as the religious-moral duties of a prince; and when, after two years' instruction, the tutor terminated his lessons, he left with the young Medici a *Trattato di morale per un principe* (Moral Treatise for a Prince).

It was expected that the scientist would also continue his work on the planned enlargement of the *Prodromus*, but he did nothing about this, for his mind was taken up with other matters. The world and its honors had ceased to hold any attraction for him, and his thoughts were centered on God alone. Recalling the words of Christ to His apostles: "I do not speak of you any more as my servants . . . I have called you my friends," he now asked himself if he should not devote his life to the priesthood.

With his usual prudence, Stensen still hesitated—also because he thought himself unworthy—and pondered long before making a decision so important. He was reassured by his confessor, Father Savignani, who told him: "God clearly wishes for you to be his minister. God always grants the necessary

101

graces to him He has chosen for a given work." This priest had long been convinced that Stensen's evident virtues and zeal for souls would lead him to the ecclesiastical state.

Stensen was so well versed in Scripture, and in moral, dogmatic and sacramental theology that, by an apostolic dispensation, no examination was required of him. His mentor in the practical liturgical preparation was Ippolito Tonnelli, a very learned teacher and regarded as a priest of unusual holiness.

Before his ordination to the priesthood, Niels went through the Spiritual Exercises of St. Ignatius and, since there seemed to be some doubt about the validity of his childhood baptism, he was re-baptized conditionally. On three consecutive days, he received the subdiaconate, the diaconate and the priesthood. The ordaining prelate was Francis, Cardinal Nerli, archbishop of Florence. On Easter Sunday, April 14, 1675, he said his first Mass in the Church of the Annunziata.

De claritate in claritatem: from light to light. This was henceforth Stensen's motto and ideal. From Cardinal Nerli we gain an insight into the manner in which he sought to put it into practice: "Since he believed that his new dignity required greater virtue, he added to his vow of chastity another vow of voluntary poverty, and to this he rigorously conformed. Of the monthly stipend of forty *scudi* provided him by the Grand Duke, Stensen spent only six *scudi* for the little food he ate and for his clothing. The rest he gave to charity."

In his striving for sanctity, he proposed to take another voluntary vow—to choose the most perfect way in everything he undertook. Impeded by his confessor, for reasons of prudence and moderation, he nevertheless applied himself with great zeal in all his activities for the greater glory of God and the good of his neighbor.

He now gave up his experiments in the natural sciences and limited himself to his task as tutor to Prince Ferdinand and to his priestly functions. He does not seem to have suffered the bitter regrets some men feel at so great a sacrifice, but felt that he was entrusted with an even greater mission. To this mission he devoted his entire life, spending all his energies in good works, self-discipline and penances. As he had done before, he continued to visit, console and aid the sick in the hospitals, prisoners in their cells, the abandoned and the needy; and he still felt that those most in need of his help were souls in sin and heresy.

Soon he became a valued confessor at the Church of San Gaëtano, then under the charge of the Theatine Fathers. Here he was besieged by penitents not only among foreigners who came to him because of his knowledge of their languages, but by numerous others attracted by his patience, charity, and wisdom. Of those same abilities he had shown in his dissections of bodies and in unveiling the secrets of nature, he now gave evidence in plumbing to the depths of souls and hearts. "It is impossible to describe," declares Cardinal Nerli, "the care and exactitude he practiced in this ministry, or the aid he gave to those who placed themselves under his spiritual direction."

Still considering that he had a special apostolate to the Jews, he tried to win their friendship, boldly entering the ghetto in an effort to convert them. He was rarely successful, but in other quarters met with a different result. Among the non-Catholic Christians he brought into the Church we find the names of the learned Wanderwaien, to whom Stensen addressed his letter "To Learned Men," published in Florence in 1675; the Flemish anatomist Tilman Trutwin, then numbered among the scientists at the Medici court; the Danish anatomist and Stensen's former pupil in Copenhagen, Holger

103

Jacobsen; his old classmate and friend of Leyden, Jan Swammerdam; the French mathematician Adrien Auzout; the Dutch patrician's son and Spinoza's pupil Albert Burgh; and the nobleman Jakob von Rautenfels.

This spiritual activity was to be but the prelude to a far greater apostolate.

VIII

Vicar Apostolic to Germany

THE RELIGIOUS CONSEQUENCES of the Thirty Years' War and of the Treaty of Westphalia (1648) reverted large sections of Germany to the status of missionary territory in the eyes of the Catholic Church. This area therefore came under the jurisdiction of the Congregation of the Propagation of the Faith in Rome, and in the middle of the seventeenth century, the Congregation established the Vicariate of the Northern Missions. This territory, which stretched over a huge area, much of it in ruins, economic as well as religious, comprised lands in northwest and east Germany to which were soon to be added Denmark and Norway.

On September 5, 1676, Bishop Valerio Maccioni, vicar apostolic of the Northern Missions, died. Thereupon Duke Johann Friedrich of Hanover proposed to Rome the name of Niels Stensen as his successor. At the same time the duke, who, as we have seen, was well acquainted with the saintly and learned Dane, informed him of the action he had taken.

In his reply of February 8, 1677, Stensen wrote that for his part he did not find the post distasteful, but he doubted the wisdom of such an appointment. He begged the duke to give the matter more thought, for there must be someone better qualified than he. He closed his letter by stating he would be happy to come to Germany as a simple missionary, if such were the will of God. Other than this, he left the decision to his ecclesiastical superiors, and while the matter was being decided in Rome, spent his time in prayer and mortification.

Meanwhile in response to the formal and official investigation of Stensen's qualifications, letters began to arrive in Rome. From Florence came a most favorable testimonial from Stensen's ecclesiastical superior, Cardinal Archbishop Nerli. The archbishop of Pisa was equally laudatory, and after speaking of Stensen's blameless life both before his conversion to Catholicism and after, added that since becoming a priest he had given proof of remarkable zeal in bringing others to the faith. Similar testimonies were received from other quarters, and among the earliest to arrive was a letter from Stensen's old friend, Bishop Opizio Pallavicini, now papal nuncio at Cologne.

We learn from a letter written by Stensen to Duke Johann Friedrich on May 1, that upon obtaining the permission of the court, he left Florence on May 1. After a midday meal, he began a pilgrimage on foot to the famous shrine of the

Holy House of Loreto, near Ancona, in order to pray for guidance. In this letter he again declared his lack of qualifications for the post offered him and said he would be glad to serve in his domains as a simple priest.

Several days before his departure from Florence he bade his friends farewell. After distributing to the poor all the money given him by Grand Duke Cosimo III to cover the expenses of his journey, he spent some time with Cardinal Nerli who considered him, as he said, "most able and knowledgeable." The cardinal subsequently wrote: "His departure from this city is a cause of regret to everyone. Not only Their Highnesses and the members of the court, who know him well as the prince's tutor, but all the people regard him as a man of real saintliness. The same is true of the religious here who have had reason to appreciate his qualities and are unanimous in declaring him a perfect model of the apostolic spirit."

On his pilgrimage to Loreto, Stensen walked barefoot and lived by alms. Knocking at the door of the poor dwellings along the way, he would ask for a piece of bread and a glass of water. If there were a priest's house in the neighborhood, he begged a night's hospitality and permission to celebrate Mass the following morning. Most often he slept beneath a tree or in some shed, for not everyone trusted this strange pilgrim. As he walked he prayed aloud, occasionally lapsing into silence as he looked upon the beauties of the landscape and meditated on God's goodness.

Pale, wasted and in tatters, he reached Loreto where he was lodged by the Penitential Fathers of the Holy House who cared for his needs and provided him a place of repose. He spent some days in making his devotions with great fervor, and then made ready to resume his journey. Ordered by the

107

superior of the Fathers at least to wear shoes, he obeyed but continued to walk the rest of the way to Rome, where he arrived on the 22nd of May.

In the Eternal City he was received with great affection and courtesy by the Tuscan grand duke's representative, the Marquess Torquato Montuoli, who presented the stained and weary pilgrim with a new wardrobe and lodgings in one of the two Medici palaces in Rome.

In expressing his gratitude to the grand duke of Tuscany, Stensen wrote: "He furnished me with an outfit far finer than seemed suitable in the eyes of God and men, and would have given me even more handsome clothing if I had not protested." In this connection Stensen went on to say that when he was staying with the Penitential Fathers of the Holy House of Loreto, he had read the life of St. Francis Xavier and was much struck by the following incident: When St. Francis set out on his voyage from Lisbon to India, he was pressed to take with him a valet whom the king of Portugal would provide, but Francis begged for the love of God to be spared this encumbrance. It was pointed out to him that he must at least take an ordinary servant, for it would diminish his authority with the other passengers, whom it would be his duty to instruct, were he to be to be seen washing his clothes at the side of the ship and preparing his meals. It was Francis' reply that it was precisely considerations of this kind which had reduced the Church of God and her prelates to the plight which preceded the Council of Trent. And to this Stensen added: "The more one deprives himself of even the necessities of life, the more one accomplishes in the interests of God."

During his sojourn in Rome, Stensen formed a firm friendship with Cardinal Gregorio Barbarigo, at one time bishop of

Bergamo and subsequently of Padua. This prelate, who was considered a model of holiness and was later to be beatified, first met Stensen in 1670 when he went to Florence on the occasion of Grand Duke Cosimo's investiture as grand master of the Order of St. Stephen. Since then the Dane had seen him several times earlier during his stays in Rome, and he now laid before the cardinal his doubts regarding his own elevation to the prelature, stressing his lack of experience in administration. The cardinal, however, who was himself an expert in diocesan organization, gave Stensen only encouragement and spent much time counseling him in the matter of a bishop's relations with clergy and laity.

In the City of the Popes, Stensen also met and received advice from François Pallu, the vicar apostolic of Tongking, a successor in the Far East of Father Alessandro Valignano, the great organizer of Jesuit missions. Nor were lay scholars lacking among the new friends Stensen made. Among them were the German mathematician Ehrenfried Walter Tschirnhausen and a young physician from the imperial city of Nuremberg in South Germany, Johann Georg Rötenbeck, who was converted under his influence and was to accompany Stensen to Hanover, where he became a priest.

On August 6, 1677, Stensen was received in private audience by Pope Innocent XI (1676–1689)—the former Benedetto Odescalchi. The Pontiff assured Stensen that it was God's will that he accept the office proposed by the Congregation of the Faith. The following day Niels wrote to Duke Johann Friedrich of Hanover: "God who made apostles of fishermen, now through the proposal of Your Serene Highness and the approval of the Holy See, manifests His will that I accept a post where angels might fear to tread; may it be that through the

109

intercession of the Holy Spirit, I will be given the light, the intention and the strength to fulfill all that is required in this task, since it was chosen for me."

As a preliminary to his consecration as a bishop, there took place on August 27, under the presidency of Cardinal Sigismund Chigi, the official inquiry into Stensen's life, character and qualifications.

From the depositions of the two prelates interpolated we cull the following observations: "During the whole time I have known Stensen, I have found him to be a man full of goodness, of an excellent mode of life, and of a laudable reputation. I have found him very erudite and most capable of teaching others. . . . I have found him to be serious, prudent and well versed in the ways of the world, and I believe that if he is nominated, he will acquit himself with honor. . . . I deem him to be worthy of the episcopate and suggest that he be given the title of titular Bishop of Titiopolis in accordance with the decree of the Congregation of the Propagation of the Faith, and that at the same time he be appointed apostolic vicar . . . I deem him capable of the important task assigned him among this heretical people for he is very learned and experienced in preaching our holy Catholic faith."

The second prelate spoke in the same terms of the candidate's life, reputation and ability, and concluded: "Here in Rome he has publicly defended certain theses, and I believe him to possess the necessary qualifications to teach as a bishop and to succeed in whatever work he may be assigned."

On September 3, Stensen moved to the headquarters of the Congregation of the Propagation of the Faith to make his pre-consecration retreat. There, for ten days he meditated, prayed and came to know those who were to be his superiors in his future work. At that time Cardinal Paluzzo Altieri was prefect

110

of the Congregation, while the important post of secretary was held by Urbano Cerri, who was then drafting a report on the state of world missions.

On September 13, at the close of his spiritual retreat, Stensen was once more received by Pope Innocent XI, this time in the palace adjacent to the basilica of Santa Maria Maggiore, and from this day dates the bull of his appointment to the titular diocese of Titiopolis. On September 19, 1667, the fifteenth Sunday after Pentecost, in the Church of the Three Magi in the Palace of the Congregation of the Propaganda, the bishop's consecration was conferred on the Danish priest-scientist. The consecrator was Cardinal Gregorio Barbarigo; Bishop François Pallu and Bishop P. A. Capobianco from southern Italy were co-consecrators.

A few days later Bishop Stensen left for Florence on horseback and arrived on the evening of September 28. The days were filled with festivities and visits with dear and old friends. One of these was Sister Flavia del Nero, to whom Stensen had written on the eve of his episcopal consecration imploring her prayers and those of her community: "Since by their prayers they brought me to God and into the Church, I now beg those prayers at the moment of entering on a position so honorable but one with such terrifying responsibilities in the sight of God, so that I may fulfill its duties to the day of my death in a manner to bring glory to the Almighty and joy to all the friends of God."

His visits in Florence over, Bishop Stensen hurriedly departed for his new field of endeavor. On October 6, he was in Venice, and on the 18th he had already reached the imperial city of Augsburg, having traversed the Alps by mail cart. From this old city, which he entered in a downpour of rain and snow, he proceeded to Frankfort on the Main, then by the river route

111

to the episcopal city of Cologne, where for several days he was the guest of Nuncio Opizio Pallavicini. As his immediate superior, the nuncio acquainted him with the duties of his new office. "His Excellency showed great affection for me in several ways, notably by the instructions he gave me," Stensen wrote to Cosimo III on October 31. "I hope to remain here for All Souls' Day, the anniversary of my birth into the Faith, and day after tomorrow to proceed to the post God has assigned to me."

On November 3, Stensen continued to Hildesheim, a town in the southern part of Duke Johann Friedrich's principality.

At Hildesheim, long noted for its historic Benedictine monastery and school, the vicar apostolic was met by the duke's chaplain, Bonaventura Nardini, a native of Garfagnani, Tuscany.

"His Serene Highness sent me to ask that you wait here until he has been informed of your arrival."

"But why?" asked Stensen, who hated any display of pomp and suspected the reason for the delay. "Would it not be better simply to proceed?"

"No, Your Excellency. Those are the Duke's orders. I am sending a courier ahead at once."

The next morning a coach and six horses appeared to transport the new vicar apostolic to Hanover, and he felt himself obliged to travel in it. On the way the coach was joined by another carrying three missionaries, and still farther on they were stopped by the duke's own coach. The bishop and the superior of the missionaries were invited to mount it and thus make their way into the city. To Stensen's still greater embarrassment, they were met on the outskirts of Hanover by the Catholic gentlemen of the court with Marshal Moltke at their head.

At his own request, the bishop spent the night at the hospice of the Capuchin Fathers. The following day he went to pay his respects to the duke and duchess, who insisted on his remaining to dine with them.

Despite this courteous welcome, the territory of Bishop Stensen, vicar apostolic of the Northern Missions, was to prove a field of tribulation, of thorns and weeds of every kind. On December 16, 1667, he wrote to the grand duke of Tuscany: "It is five weeks since I arrived at my post. If it were my vocation to lead a genteel and comfortable life, I would have no cause to complain; in fact I would be very happy. But the spiritual misery not only of Catholics but also of those who profess to be Catholics makes me fear that I too will lose my soul with theirs. His Serene Highness presses upon me the gift of a coach and six horses. I am doing my best to decline the offer, preferring two donkeys after the example of my patron, St. Nicholas."

Duke Johann Friedrich granted Bishop Stensen in his capacity as court bishop an annual stipend of 1,000 thalers, which he wished to make retroactive to the preceding Easter, and assigned to him a private house and chapel. In fact he was ready to do anything for him, and soon came to share the opinion of Father Paolo Oliva, general of the Jesuits, who had written him prior to Bishop Stensen's arrival: "In him you receive one born a subject of the Queen of Denmark, your sister, and an angel reborn in the Catholic faith; a true image of the apostles in the purity of his morals, in his understanding, and in his apostolic zeal. And yet, these riches of mind and soul are matched in him by Christian humility, so that he lives and works as though he were a simple member of the clergy and not a mitred prelate. I, myself, never talked with him without being confounded by the modesty of his behavior, the fervor of

113

his faith and his endeavor to look for nothing else in the world but God. . . . In the first conversation with this personage, Your Highness will realize how deficient is my attempt to picture this man who here in Rome is regarded as a pattern of virtue and a fountainhead of wisdom."

All this was perfectly true, but the new vicar apostolic soon found the spiritual climate of the court of Hanover much colder than in Florence. The task before him was far from encouraging, as we learn from his words: "Here there are many places where Catholics have no opportunity to practice their religion; in others there are abominable scandals. There is a great lack of secular priests available for the missions; in fact I have only one. Among the Jesuits and the Capuchins we have some good men, but the devil has placed such ideas into the heads of both Catholics and non-Catholics about these good religious that one has only to mention the name of their orders, to have the listener recoil.

"Not only non-Catholics but quite a few Catholics are so prejudiced against the Society of Jesus that they will have nothing to do with its members unless obliged by necessity. Remembering as I do the role played by these Fathers in my conversion and spiritual direction, I am much distressed by the harm accomplished by such prejudices when I see their actions and words misrepresented in letters and conversations.

"As for the Capuchins, the Catholics do not show so much dislike toward them. The Lutherans, however, are revolted by their austere practices, and this hostility persists even after the same Lutherans have been converted. This is due perhaps to a natural desire for bodily comforts and to a dislike of seeing others deprive themselves of them.

"Certain lay people claim that the Jesuits want to take over everything, and in one letter I recently received the writer says

114

this is their tendency everywhere. In addition to all this, every time one wants to send another regular or secular priest to some place where one or two of these orders is established, dissensions immediately follow.

"The majority of the Catholic people here are so cold in the expression of their faith that I fear I shall soon lose the little warmth I had transmitted to me by those warmer servants of God in Italy."

The objections against the Jesuits and Capuchins reported to Bishop Stensen did not change his good opinion of them, and he was on very friendly terms with both. The center of Catholic life in Hanover prior to his arrival was the Capuchin hospice directly connected with the palace chapel where, in 1677, twelve Capuchins lived in their cells, and conducted divine services and preached in German, Italian and French. As for the members of the Society of Jesus, despite their heroic sacrifices and labors in Germany, their fortunes were at a low ebb, and they had made powerful enemies because of their support of Roman claims for church property confiscated during the second period of the Thirty Years' War. Cognizant of their worth, Bishop Stensen defended them against the charges of certain laymen, sent them on missions to various districts and helped them establish a school in the free imperial city of Hamburg.

While in Rome, during the summer of 1677, prior to his consecration as bishop, Stensen had written a long report to the Congregation of the Propaganda regarding the condition of Catholicism in his native city of Copenhagen, basing it on his own experience there as royal anatomist between the years 1672 and 1674. It was upon his advice that Duke Johann Friedrich had appointed an Italian Catholic, Francesco Floramonti, as his envoy to Copenhagen to the great benefit of the Catholic community. The Mass and other divine services could now be conducted not only in the chapels of the Spanish and French envoys but also in that of the duke of Hanover.

Pope Innocent XI had been very much impressed with Stensen's report to the Propaganda and on March 14, 1678, less than four months after his arrival in Hanover, the Pontiff extended the powers of the vicar apostolic to include Denmark and Norway. Stensen accepted and was able to bring about something of a Catholic revival in Copenhagen. Among other measures he procured financial support for the Jesuits there, and even managed to add to their staff. In 1679 some 800 Communions were received at Easter in the various chapels of the city. Also in May, 1676, two months after the extension of Bishop Stensen's vicariate to Norway, the first Mass since the Protestant Reformation was celebrated in that Scandinavian country, and during the following years several Jesuit missionaries were active there.

One of Bishop Stensen's difficulties in shouldering his vast responsibilities was the lack of funds. Not that it mattered to him personally, for he had taken a voluntary vow of poverty and would have cheerfully begged his bread from day to day. "I am hoping for some help," he wrote to the cardinals of the Propaganda, "for the good of the souls entrusted to me. I do not want to discourage those who are favorably disposed to Catholicism by having them see converts to our faith obliged to sink below the station in life they occupied as Lutherans. Neither do I want to see them reduced by necessity to living with relatives and placed in danger of losing their faith. It is difficult for such newcomers to the faith to be deprived of priests and sacraments and daily subjected to pressure by relatives and friends. For example, a woman here who became a

116

Catholic remained staunch in her decision so long as she continued to live with Catholics, but on returning to her home, she was mistreated by her relatives and even threatened and beaten by her own mother. Although she persevered for some time, she finally renounced her faith, married a Lutheran and returned to Lutheranism herself."

When the Congregation of the Propaganda replied that it was not the custom for it to grant subsidies to those who joined the Church and that this could not be done for obvious reasons, the poor vicar apostolic tried in other quarters to obtain funds. Among others, he wrote to Cosimo de' Medici: "The Duke of Hanover gives me a thousand thalers a year and fourteen thalers each week. Of this I use for myself only what is strictly necessary; even so, I cannot satisfy the needs of those in want, and have to leave in suspense many who would enter the Church had they some assurance of material help. . . . Many Lutheran parents have asked me to take their children and raise them in our religion, but I am obliged to refuse many of these requests, for I have no means to support these children."

His greatest regret was that the Catholics spread over this vast territory under his charge could not receive sufficient spiritual care because of the lack of priests. He himself went to the utmost limit of his strength to supply their needs, traveling about constantly, giving no thought to bad weather nor to his health. Everywhere he went he pleaded for missionaries to help him.

Each time he found a man sufficiently instructed and with a leaning toward the priesthood, he did not hesitate, after making careful examination and inquiry, to ordain him. Nevertheless, in spite of his precautions, the thought of having ordained someone who was not worthy haunted him—even on his death-bed. "The ordination of priests," he wrote to Cosimo III in 1683, "is so important a matter that it seems to me that in view of conditions in this country a bishop's very salvation depends on it." And in a letter to Signora Arnolfini, he said: "I have already ordained a great number and, to my shame, I have later come to realize that several among them were not worthy and that I should have discovered this and excluded them beforehand had I been more vigilant in carrying out my duty. Pray and have others pray that God will not damn me for their sins and for my own."

Like other saintly souls who place every moment of their lives in the service of God, Stensen believed he had accomplished nothing. Nevertheless during those two years as vicar apostolic, he made many conversions through his preaching, his pastoral visits and his writings.

During this period he published the following works:

Examen objectionis circa diversas scripturas sacras (Hanover, 1678). This was the development of his letter to Sylvius written in 1670, concerning the authority of the Church and the interpretation of Scripture.

Occasio sermonum de religione cum Joanne Silvio (Hanover, 1678), a continued discussion of various religious questions with the Dutch Protestants begun in 1670 in Amsterdam and with the same Sylvius.

A tract in German, *Catholische Glaubens-Lehr*, in which he answered other Protestant objections (also published in 1678).

De Purgatorio (Hanover, 1678), an important treatise explaining the Catholic doctrine on this subject.

Defensio scrutinii reformatorum (Hanover, 1679), in which he defended and explained his objection to the teachings of the Reformers.

Defensio et plenior elucidatio epistolae de propria conver-

sione (Hanover, 1680), in which he set forth, in answer to J. W. Bayer, a professor at Jena, his reasons for joining the Catholic Church, dealt with apologetic questions concerning Bible and Church, with further sections on syncretism and Cartesianism, and with the question of sanctity.

In all these as in other of Stensen's writings, the reader is given an insight not only into the relationship between science and faith but more deeply into the relation of the truly scientific mind which works by methodical observation and verification and the theological mind that builds its conclusions upon authority and tradition. To these was added the mind of a saintly man who put the theological conclusions into practice in his daily life.

He worked without ceasing, for he believed that "everyone, whether he be priest or layman, is called to perfection in his state of life. This means he must lose no time in idle words, but must plan each hour and each minute of a day for which he must account to God."

He renounced all diversions and recreation, and every comfort. Later Niccolò Francesco Graziani and his wife, Maria Teresa de Verges, who lived at the court of Hanover in Stensen's time, were to declare under oath:

"The life of this prelate, so far as food and clothing were concerned, was that of the poorest of the poor. One would not have known who he was save for the woolen cassock he wore, and he refused any other from the very first days of his vicariate when his predecessor's robes were offered him at a very low price.

"He accepted a large stipend from His Highness the Duke, who granted it to him for his proper upkeep; but he used it all for the poor to whom he gave away everything he could, and this was true the whole time we knew him.

"He led an exhausting life, each day celebrating Holy Mass

119

in public in the chapel of the Duke, and this in an exemplary manner. Often on feastdays he gave a sermon from the altar. On the afternoon of feasts he preached again, sometimes in French, sometimes in German, sometimes in Italian, and always with great effect on his hearers. He used these various languages because persons of all these nationalities were present at the court.

"He took part in no amusements, and fled those offered at the court. He frequented the court only in deference to Their Highnesses, to preach and win souls, and everywhere wore his woolen cassock, although Hanover was a Lutheran city. We declare all this under oath, having been witnesses to what we have stated."

This deposition was made at Lucca on January 14, 1700.

IX

In Hanover and Münster

"MY STATE OF LIFE presupposes a perfect man, but I find myself buried beneath my imperfections. . . . Perhaps I am the unfruitful occupant of a position for which the Lord has already foreseen someone else who will be more productive. . . . From the scant progress that I am making among the Catholics, the little help that I am able to give to the poor, and my frequent shortcomings which are impeding the conversion of non-Catholics, I begin to fear for my salvation, and feel myself obliged to think of making certain decisions."

These words reveal Bishop Stensen as undergoing a period of

desolation and uncertainty. He was deeply conscious of his great responsibility toward souls, ever mindful of the fact he would have to answer to God for every one who through his negligence or other fault had missed the opportunity of being converted, or, after being converted, had fallen away. He was even thinking of retiring to a monastery to do penance for his own faults and to pray for sinners. He wrote: "Here the winter has been extremely hard, but souls are colder still, and there seems no way to open them to the warmth of God's love. I cannot blame the extent of this sickness on those who suffer from it, but on my ignorance, incompetence and negligence, since God called me here as the physician. I am more culpable in my resistance to the divine graces God gives me to permit me to conform to the dignity He has bestowed upon me than are these people here who might not resist the inspiration God would give them if I were properly fulfilling my ministry."

As he fought his way out of his spiritual desert, Stensen came to the conclusion that it was not possible for one person adequately to provide for all the religious needs of the huge vicariate assigned him. In his report to the Congregation of the Propagation of the Faith on January 23, 1679, he declared that for physical, financial and political reasons, he could not do justice to all the territories entrusted to his charge. The following May he was relieved by the Propaganda of his responsibilities other than for the vicariates of Brunswick, Hamburg and Denmark.

Our missionary took comfort, and was able to make new and notable conversions. Unfortunately, the death of Duke Johann Friedrich of Hanover, which occurred on December 28, 1679, as the prince was on his way to Italy, made many changes. The duke was succeeded by his brother, Duke Ernst August, and

122

both he and his wife were Protestants. The religious consequences were that Protestantism now became the state religion,
the court chapel was no longer available for Catholic services,
and the adjoining Capuchin hospice was closed.

Otherwise the new prince was favorably disposed toward his
Catholic subjects, and elsewhere in the city they were allowed
freedom of worship and their services were continued. In this
connection, Stensen wrote to Cosimo III: "We are able to say
that no one could expect better treatment from a non-Catholic
prince and under the conditions prevailing in this country. He
has, moreover, a good opinion of the Catholic religion, and
publicly acknowledges its good effects. He assures me that if in
conscience he could be as sure of the necessity of the Catholic
religion as he is of its quality, there is nothing that would prevent him from embracing it."

Thus things went smoothly until difficulties arose regarding
two of the Capuchin priests. As the duke had closed their
hospice and forbidden them to go about in their habits among
non-Catholics, ten of the Capuchins left Hanover, but two
remained behind. These two Capuchins no longer wore their
robes and cowls and lived in the house of a man of dubious
reputation. The vicar apostolic saw them exposed to grave dan-
gers and disapproved their wearing secular dress. "I remember," he wrote, "that St. Francis de Sales said that the first
duty of a religious is attachment to the observance of his rule,
and that its voluntary infringement is dangerous to their salvation." For this reason, and carrying out the instructions of the
papal nuncio in Cologne whom he consulted, he told the Fathers to join their brethren elsewhere, since it was the nuncio's
wish to reorganize the mission in Hanover and place it in the

123

charge of other missionary priests. He finally persuaded the two Capuchins to return to their rule of life and mode of dress, and to leave the city.

In this painful occurrence, Stensen displayed admirable tact and patience. He wrote to the Capuchin provincial deploring the circumstances, and added: "Had my superiors ordered me to place the entire mission, as well as myself personally, under the direction of the Capuchin Fathers, I would gladly have done so and have seen God's will in their decision."

Never at any time did he refuse to accede to his superiors' instructions. Thus, although he would willingly have reverted to the status of a poor and simple missionary, he obeyed at once when by a papal brief of October 7, 1680, he was directed to go to Münster where he was appointed auxiliary to the bishop of Paderborn and Münster. As a matter of fact, this second diocese had been placed under his charge several months earlier. When, in 1678, Bernard von Galen, bishop of Münster, died, the bishopric had passed under the ecclesiastical and political jurisdiction of the prince bishop of Paderborn, Ferdinand von Fürstenberg. Bishop von Galen had taken effective steps to enforce sound decrees in accordance with the provisions of the Council of Trent, but had not had time to institute a thoroughgoing reform. Internally the bishopric remained weak in many ways. Bishop von Fürstenberg had tried to remedy the weakness but had met with little success—due to the fact that his own see of Paderborn demanded much attention and he himself was in poor health. He felt the need of an auxiliary and had requested the Congregation of the Propaganda in Rome for Stensen's appointment.

From Hanover, Bishop Stensen proceeded to Neuhaus where he introduced himself at the residence of the prince bishop. He then went for spiritual refreshment to the Jesuit College in Paderborn. Here again we note in the spiritual life of Stensen a strong attachment to the Jesuit and Ignatian spirituality. That he had the example of the early Jesuits before his eyes in his reforms may be proved from a letter written prior to his departure from Hanover for his new field of endeavor. In a letter dated April 5, 1680, he said: "To provide foreign countries with missionaries, we should need personalities and missionaries like St. Ignatius and his companions, like St. Francis Xavier, St. Peter Faber and others, who would travel from one end of the world to the other with breviary and staff, begging from place to place for alms as their only traveling money. . . ."

He had followed this example himself. As we know, before his episcopal consecration he had traveled to Rome on foot, living by alms on the way. As vicar apostolic and auxiliary bishop he often walked long distances to save the fare for the poor.

Methodical himself, he had a special liking for the Spiritual Exercises of St. Ignatius, which he now made before his formal installation as auxiliary bishop of Münster. The Exercises gave his spiritual life the basic feature of always giving first place in his thoughts to God's will. One of his maxims testifies to this: "Before all, we must . . . desire that God's will may be done in everything; thus union with God will be maintained."

It may be supposed that he also owed to the Spiritual Exercises his faithfulness to mental prayer, which he practiced for one hour each morning. In beginning his prayers, he placed himself in God's presence; on perceiving that he had suffered a distraction, he beat his breast to show his repentance. All these practices derive from advice given in the book of the Spiritual Exercises of St. Ignatius. Thence also his painstaking daily examination of conscience and his detestation of every, even the smallest, sin.

In Hanover, Bishop Stensen had lived in strict simplicity with two of the young men he had converted in Florence and who had accompanied him to Germany—the anatomist Jakob Rautenfels and the physician Johann Georg Rötenbeck. Now in Münster they again lived in austerity under the same roof, their residence a great bare house, open to the winds and in an isolated part of the city, which was the deanery of St. Ludgeri's collegiate church. Twelve canons were on the staff of this church which was the spiritual center of some 2,000 souls. This deanship assured Bishop Stensen of an extra prebend so that his combined annual income reached to the neighborhood of 800 thalers.

This sum did not suffice the auxiliary bishop for the charitable needs of his pastorate. Besides furnishing food and lodging to converts who would otherwise have been homeless and penniless after their change of religion, he opened his heart to all others in misfortune. For instance, three small children were found abandoned and sleeping in the open; Stensen paid for a month's lodging for them at an inn. A widow, reduced to poverty, was roaming the outskirts of the city and on the point of committing suicide when Bishop Stensen came to her aid. One day on leaving the church he was surrounded by two men and three women on the point of collapse from lack of food. How could he send them away?

What he could not do himself, he tried to interest others in doing, seeking their aid for the poor, the abandoned, and the persecuted. In their behalf he constantly importuned his superiors, the Congregation of the Propagation of the Faith, the grand duke of Tuscany, and his other friends. He wrote to Ortensio Mauri, the secretary of the prince bishop: "In Hanover I became accustomed to distributing the alms given me each year by His Serene Highness for this purpose, and it breaks my heart to have to send these people away, and in them to see the poor Christ departing unconsoled."

Unfortunately his disbursements exceeded his income. He said to the same friend: "If I organized my life according to prudence, I would consider myself at fault, because I have almost always given away more than I receive. Yet God has always come to my aid, either through unexpected gifts from persons I had not counted on, or by allowing me to meet others who gave me alms to dispense. This has happened again and again over a period of several years, and now I find I am unable to make a rule for what I give away. When someone comes to me in grave need, or when a soul is in danger, it seems to me that even if I have no money and am in debt, it would be lacking in confidence in God's goodness if I did not risk a further debt. . . . Meanwhile, I can conscientiously say that I have never kept for myself anything other than the bare necessities."

He even sold possessions to which he was attached. "I still have some silver objects such as a holy water font for which I can get at least fifty thalers, and an old gilt chalice which I would willingly sell were someone looking for a chalice for some church—or for a holy water font for a cathedral, since the one I have is quite large and fine. It consoles me to see that God is preparing me, as I hope, for that state of Christian poverty I have always desired. Since I am on my way, I seek to free myself from everything not necessary for my duties. I only ask God to free me from my debts, first toward Him, and then toward men. I would be happy if He wished to take me from the world; if He still has use for me here, I am equally satisfied. God alone—and we have all!"

He was advised to reduce the number of those he sheltered in his house to the few necessary personnel. He would have been quite content with one curate and one servant, but he

127

did not know where to begin because all others who lived under his roof were extremely poor. In the meanwhile, he cut down on food: "We have reformed our table, and will reform it even more to the degree their strength permits. I cannot reduce them all at once to what I myself find sufficient, for I have been accustomed to a small amount of food for a long time."

He was much concerned about his debts, which amounted to several hundred thalers and because he felt his improvidence had "violated justice." To the secretary of the Propaganda he wrote: "I have finally been obliged to reduce my expenses, and to abandon several converts whom I kept at my table up until Easter time by selling certain sacred objects I had kept since the time I was vicar apostolic in Hanover."

The diocese of Münster covered a vast area, and its spiritual level was very low. If it could be called a Catholic oasis in the midst of the sands of Protestantism, it could not be said that the oasis contained either palms or springs. Most of the Catholics were ignorant, there was much corruption among the young, and religious laxity prevailed. "I fear that in the end," the prelate wrote, "they will be lost to the Church. . . . If the powerful non-Catholics who surround this diocese were to occupy this section by force, it would be shown that it mattered little to most people to what religion they belonged."

The clergy of Münster were not, on the whole, models of virtue. A number of them lived a worldly life, and some were even ashamed of their ecclesiastical dress and tonsure. They loved good cheer and gave little care to the religious instruction of the people. For some years they had been left to their own devices and had received scant attention from the episcopal authority. There had been no visitation of parishes, and in some places the sacrament of Confirmation had not been conferred for twenty or thirty years.

We should take into consideration the fact that Bishop Ferdinand von Fürstenberg was constantly ill over a period of several years. But if his poor health excused him from visiting his diocese, he and his predecessors would appear to be more at fault in conferring holy orders on unworthy subjects, candidates presented or imposed by powerful families and usually with a large benefice in view.

To strive for his sanctification and that of others was Stensen's constant preoccupation; he was completely without self-interest or any earthly ambition. It is not surprising to find him practicing devotion to the Sacred Heart of Jesus. When in 1677 (two scant years after the apparition to Sister Margaret Mary Alacoque) he was consecrated bishop in Rome, he had taken as his episcopal arms a heart surmounted by a cross.

Parish visitations, the spiritual direction of a convent of fifteen nuns, charitable work among the poor and desolate, the catechetical instruction of the people, and the direction of the large deanery of St. Ludgeri, occupied his every waking hour. So overwhelmed was he with work that in the fall of 1681, he decided to give up the deanship in order to devote his full time to his duties as a bishop of the diocese, and on October 4, he resigned his charge of St. Ludgeri. This entailed the loss of the prebend, but as he explained in a letter to Cosimo III, the bishopric of Münster was so large it was not possible for one man to be dean and auxiliary bishop at the same time.

As auxiliary bishop of Münster, Stensen bent every effort to implement the decrees of the Council of Trent regarding the visitation of parishes, the life of the clergy, the duties of prelates, the holding of synods, the cumulation of benefices, meet-

129

ings of the regular clergy, and their mode of life. First on his list was the administration of the sacraments of Confirmation and Holy Orders. Since Confirmation had been neglected for over twenty years in many parts of the bishopric, even in the immediate suburbs of the city, Bishop Stensen rectified this by conferring the sacrament in some 200 parishes during the three years he was in Münster (1680–1683); in other words, in almost eighty percent of the churches. He raised the requirements for the examination of candidates to the priesthood in accordance with the Tridentine decrees and abolished as an abuse all fees in connection with ordination.

This spiritual renewal of his flock often entailed visitations with full ecclesiastical and secular authority. His efforts at reform and adherence to details were so noticeable that his good example began to spread beyond the confines of his bishopric. There were, however, members of the clergy who, in order to cover their own shortcomings, tried to label him with the tag of scrupulosity.

Bishop Stensen nevertheless continued on his chosen path. He kept in close touch with the members of the various religious orders within his jurisdiction; he consecrated abbots, assisted at the clothing ceremonies of nuns; and was a frequent guest at the Jesuit College of Münster. Here he more than once celebrated pontifical high Mass in the Jesuit church in honor of St. Ignatius and St. Francis Xavier. Here, too, he went to confession.

In his capacity as vicar apostolic, Bishop Stensen continued to exercise his influence throughout the other German and Danish territories under his jurisdiction. He eased the position of the Catholic mission in Hamburg by asking Grand Duke Cosimo to effect the appointment of a Tuscan envoy in the

130

person of the anatomist Theodor Kerckring, Stensen's old friend and fellow-student at Leyden. His friendship with the tolerant Duke Ernst August of Hanover made it possible for the Jesuits of Hildesheim to hold divine services in two chapels in Neustadt and Altstadt. In his native Copenhagen three Catholic chapels continued open and supplied with priests, and the first Catholic mission station outside the Danish capital was opened in Fredericia, a military garrison. In the spring of 1683, he sent his faithful Johann Georg Rötenbeck, now an ordained priest, to Mecklenburg in East Elbia.

There is scarcely need to say that in his diocese of Münster he found a goodly number of abuses to suppress, negligence and apathy to condemn, also a few cases—perhaps four to five —requiring ecclesiastical discipline. Although he enjoyed the esteem of many well-disposed persons, his relations were not smooth with some members of the higher clergy, especially the vicar general of Münster, Johannes von Alpen. Not only was there a lack of zealous priests, but appointments continued to be made with regard to a man's noble birth, thereby restricting the higher clergy to certain families. Although Bishop Stensen tried to correct this abuse, he met with strong opposition from his canons with Von Alpen at their head. As long as the prince bishop of Paderborn lived there were rumblings, but no open break.

Bishop Stensen was on no better terms with the vicar general of Paderborn, the Benedictine Laurentius von Dript. The two came to a head-on collision when Bishop Stensen, who had been appointed apostolic commissioner by Rome, consecrated the lawfully elected Abbot Pantaleon Mönnich as against Von Dript's candidate. There followed a feud of the written word. In one of these letters, Bishop Stensen admonished the Benedictine vicar general in these words: "Court life is always a peril, Most Reverend Father, but especially so for a member of a religious order."

When the prince bishop sided with his vicar general, Bishop Stensen showed his superior respect and loyalty, but remained steadfast. This was not the first time that the Prince Bishop of Paderborn, Ferdinand von Fürstenberg, was crossed by Bishop Stensen in a matter of abbatial consecration. Nevertheless, Von Fürstenberg, who respected the high principles of his auxiliary, gave him more and more authority and assigned him one visitation after another.

Bishop Stensen knew that many notable ecclesiastics had little sympathy with him, and he said: "They call me scrupulous and accuse me of severity. They never think of the terrible judgment which nevertheless is true: if a bishop fulfills two-thirds of his obligations, he is a saint in the eyes of men; but if he does not add to this the other third, he is condemned in the eyes of God. Only one thing sustains me; it is to know that I came here and will remain so long as I am under the order of superiors, even if I have to beg my bread from door to door. I have no other end in view than God's glory and the salvation of souls."

Out of solicitude for his priests whom he had come to know as the result of his numerous pastoral visits, Bishop Stensen wrote in Münster a treatise entitled *Parochorum hoc age* in which he specifies the duties of individual pastoral care. He sent the manuscript to Cosimo III and the work was published in Florence at the grand duke's expense. The book begins by comparing the holiness of Christians in the primitive Church with the lukewarmness of Christians of the time. The author expresses the opinion that this was in great part the fault of priests, who should think not only of their personal sanctification but also of the sanctity of souls entrusted to their care. Whatever the reception given this treatise, it is a fact that Stensen's German ecclesiastical superior, the prince bishop of Paderborn, showed an increasing confidence in his auxiliary bishop. He nevertheless admonished him not to be too severe and enlisted the friendly cooperation of Stensen's confessor, the Jesuit Johann Sterck. The latter directed Bishop Stensen to be a little less rigorous with himself and with others.

"It seems," Father Sterck wrote in a letter in Latin, "that Your Lordship is troubled because your numerous duties prevent you from the earlier practice of your devotions; also because after all your efforts there are so few conversions. . . . What should one do? I myself had the same doubts regarding my work at our college and on the mission. Finally, however, I considered that it was better to put aside my devotions and the comfort I derived from them than for souls to perish. If one can save a single soul, all the fatigue, the effort and the pains are abundantly rewarded.

"We must sometimes leave God for God. . . . If the result does not correspond to the effort, we may console ourself by the thought that it is up to us to plant and water, and that it is for God to cause our work to sprout and grow. . . . I repeat: it is for us to pray, to plant, to toil, to gather up, to exhort, to supply, and then to place everything in God's hands. For this reason, I recommend to Your Lordship that you proceed in the way you have begun and not to glance back."

With regard to the severity for which Bishop Stensen was criticized, Father Sterck told him: "I believe Your Lordship would be more successful if he were a little less rigorous. To wish to change all at once customs and ways of life rooted in Germany for many centuries appears hard and difficult. Unhappily many things have crept in which one cannot approve,

133

but one breath cannot blow them away. We must count on time and opportunity—many things can be changed little by little. It is not possible to go from one extreme to the other.

"I wish that Your Lordship—pray forgive my frankness—would follow in the footsteps of St. Francis de Sales rather than those of St. Charles of Borromeo—or rather that you would combine the spirit of the one with the other.

"If we wanted to draw a parallel between the Christians of today and those of the first golden century, we could scarcely call ourselves Christian. Let us be content to save those we can. Your Lordship is not bound in conscience to require that everything be carried out with the maximum of exactitude. Certainly it is preferable for everything to be perfect. But in proceeding with moderation, it may be hoped that what is lacking in intensity may be compensated by extension; in other words, that what is less perfect may be compensated by numbers. What can be done for the mediocre is still laudable."

X

Tribulations

Bishop Stensen had foreseen for some time that his duties as auxiliary bishop of Münster would be of short duration, given the sad state of health of the prince bishop, who suffered from a severe renal complaint. Over a period of two years the prelate had often seemed close to death, and on June 27, 1683, Stensen wrote to Cosimo III:

"Yesterday morning, at 6 o'clock our time, the Prince Bishop of Münster and Paderborn, His Lordship Ferdinand von Fürstenberg, died at Neuhaus. May God grant him every lasting happiness. He suffered a great martyrdom in this life; we trust this was his purgatory!"

135

The death of a man of high position is often like the sinking of a ship which drags down men and objects in its wake. Very soon the auxiliary bishop saw mounting in his direction waves of resentment on the part of those he had displeased for various reasons and who would gladly have seen the meticulous foreigner return to his own country.

In his will, Prince Bishop von Fürstenberg had appointed Bishop Stensen *ad interim* vicar apostolic of the entire Northern Vicariate, and bequeathed to him a personal gift. However, the chapter of the cathedral of Münster, to which at the death of a bishop the jurisdiction of the diocese was transferred, elected the dean of the chapter and vicar general, Canon Johann Rodger von Torck, as administrator.

On the morning of August 3, 1683, Bishop Stensen received from the chapter a letter forbidding him in bold terms to exercise any authority in the diocese, permitting him only to pontificate at certain ceremonies, and curtailing his visitations of churches and monasteries. Moreover, the chapter threatened recourse to severe measures if in future the auxiliary did not refrain from expressing the "indiscreet and offensive" opinions he had voiced in a letter against the dean of the chapter.

What had happened was this: Bishop Stensen had taken disciplinary action regarding a convent of religious from Lorraine. In this community of teaching nuns, living according to the Augustinian rule, there was much dissension. To restore order and discipline, Bishop Stensen had transferred the nun mainly at fault and a troublemaker, to an Augustinian convent with stricter enclosure. Now this nun happened to be the sister of the secretary of the chapter, and it is easy to imagine the latter's anger and the campaign he led against the prelate. The members of the chapter sided with the nun and the vindictive secretary, whom they feared even though he was subordinate to them. The dean of the chapter, Von Torck, had first agreed with the bishop's handling of the matter, but after the death of the prince bishop, he allowed the nun to return to her former convent.

Stensen, with his usual zeal but in quite courteous terms, had expressed his dissatisfaction to the dean on seeing the secretary and the troublemaking nun thus unjustly protected, and ended his letter: "When it is a question of God and of souls, we should not be below the pagans who do not condone even those of their own blood when they violate justice."

Bishop Stensen bowed before the injunctions of the chapter, not wishing to embark on a useless discussion, and putting into practice his own precepts regarding humility: "A humble man offends no one, and does not engage in quarrels. After stating his reasons, he yields modestly."

In the same letter to the dean and vicar general he said: "The election of the new prince bishop is at hand. It is the most important matter, because on it depends the salvation or loss of the diocese. The enemy of Christianity is at the very heart of the Holy Roman Empire, and we should appease God by rooting out any scandals." (These were the days when the imperial armies, consisting of forces from most of the German principalities, were joining with those of the king of Poland, John Sobieski, and of Prince Eugene of Savoy, to do battle against the Turks who were besieging Vienna.)

Because he feared for the future welfare of this important Catholic bastion in Northern Germany, Stensen felt compelled to inform Rome of what was happening. On July 20, 1683, he wrote direct to Pope Innocent XI a long report on the situation in the diocese, a report which he prudently decided to present to the Pontiff through his old friend Cardinal Barbarigo.

From a letter he wrote later to the cardinals of the Congregation of the Propagation of the Faith we have the details of the sordid struggle conducted by those in authority against Bishop Stensen at this time, not only in grave matters but in small slighting ways. For example, at ceremonies in which he pontificated in the cathedral he was assigned as assistants two clergy in minor orders, a violation of the canonical rules.

He took note of everything but said nothing. Writing to Cosimo III in regard to the coming election, he said: "May God grant us a good election. As we are on the far confines of the Catholic Church, the holiness of the clergy is more necessary than in any other place." In his report of July 20, to Pope Innocent XI, he had expressed the same hope: "If God does not give us a pastor who recognizes the necessity, and wishes and is able to give himself entirely to governing the diocese in spiritual matters, I foresee that the faith will be destroyed here and divine worship completely abandoned."

Rome's reaction to his report was a letter despatched by the Cardinal Secretary of State to the papal nuncio at Cologne, Ercole Visconti, who had succeeded Opizio Pallavicini. The nuncio was reminded in the name of the Sovereign Pontiff that at the forthcoming election he should bear in mind the greater glory of the Church and its need of a worthy and capable shepherd in Münster.

However, in that city the intrigues of the chapter under Von Torck's leadership made almost certain the election of Maximilian Heinrich von Bayern, archbishop-elector of Cologne. In this, Von Torck was aided and abetted by the archbishop's councilor, Wilhelm Lothar Ducker, who secured the votes of the members of the Münster chapter by promises of offices, benefices and money. The archbishop-elector was himself a devout and moral priest, but not the personage needed for the office. One of those princely ecclesiastics who habitually ignored the obligation of pastoral visitations, he preferred to stay at home and leave it to the papal nuncio to administer the sacraments of Confirmation and Holy Orders in the territories under his jurisdiction. In addition to the archdiocese of Cologne, the archbishop-elector already had under his care the dioceses of Hildesheim and Liége.

To avoid any further difficulties with the chapter, Bishop Stensen who had neither a seat nor a vote in the election, decided to leave Münster for a time and engage elsewhere in his duties as vicar apostolic. "On the eve of the election," he wrote, "having understood that everything was already settled and that I would be requested to say the Mass of the Holy Spirit at the opening of the election, I left the city before receiving the formal invitation, and now I am en route to my apostolic vicariates. . . . If God does not perform a miracle, the factions will be hard to reconcile, for each will try to protect his own interests and those of his followers. For the moment I do not see that anyone is thinking of the public good. Such is the pity of human blindness!"

The election of Maximilian Heinrich von Bayern took place on September 1, "with much scandal in the matter of securing votes, and with so little secrecy that even women and servants were discussing it."

On the journey he now began from Münster to Hamburg, Stensen wore secular dress, since he was passing through territories where the wearing of ecclesiastical garb was forbidden. In the mail coach he overheard with indignation and shame

139

the conversations of his non-Catholic traveling companions regarding the election of the prince bishop; from them he learned the enormous sums spent in buying votes.

He wrote to Nuncio Ercole Visconti in Cologne: "The election cannot be approved in the eyes of God. It is stained by open simony. I have not merely picked rumors out of the air; my main information has been obtained from certain men worthy of credence. I do not speak personally of the one who has been elected—I am aware of the respect due my superiors. I refer solely to the methods employed by the administrators, and I am certain that if His Serene Highness the Prince Elector knew the details of his election, he would himself hold it in abomination."

In his reply to Bishop Stensen, under date of September 17, Nuncio Visconti, who seems to have been remarkably ill-informed about the situation, stated that the facts appeared to be quite different. "His Serene Highness' probity and the integrity of his life and morals are so well known and respected that no one could admit that he would knowingly allow the slightest illegality in his election. It must certainly be deduced that if any fault were committed, it could not be imputed to him." The nuncio was inclined to take an optimistic view, but prudently ended by telling Bishop Stensen that he would leave the matter in abeyance until he had been informed exactly of what had transpired by Stensen and others.

On October 2, 1683, Bishop Stensen sent a long letter on the situation in Münster to the cardinals of the Propaganda in which he entered into details regarding the mismanagement of the archdiocese, the prohibitions of the chapter, the matter of the Augustinian nuns, and the encroachments of Von Torck, the vicar general, against whom he listed nine points of complaint. In view of this and other information sent to Rome by Bishop Stensen, papal confirmation of the election of the bishop of Münster was delayed. After a few months the Holy See, supported by the German emperor, Archbishop Maximilian Heinrich's suzerain in the temporal sphere, took a firm stand and demanded the resignation of the archbishop-elector. One reason given was that one who already administered an archdiocese and two bishoprics should not take over another. The Holy See's protests were ignored, but the Pope held firm in his demand. Eventually the problem received a peaceful solution through the death of Archbishop Maximilian Heinrich and the election of Friedrich Christian von Plettenberg, which was immediately confirmed by Rome.

Already long before these happenings, Bishop Stensen had considered giving up his post as auxiliary bishop, not because of its arduous tasks but because he considered himself ill-equipped to carry out his duties. As early as the end of March, 1683, he had written to the secretary of the Propaganda, Bishop Odoardo Cibo: "It seems to me clear that my vocation is for the missions. In my duties as auxiliary I suffer much anguish in regard to the matter of ordinations, because of the corruption of youth and the difficulty in arriving at any certainty as to the life and morals of the candidates. Already I see here among those I have ordained a few who conduct themselves in such a way that I wish I had not been the bishop to ordain them."

He went so far as to accuse himself of ignorance: "The most certain way for the good of my own soul and the souls of others would be to allow me to spend two years at the College of the Propaganda and to acquire a solid foundation through study.

141

During the last six years I have spent my time working for others without really applying myself to the development of my spiritual life or to study."

Yet this was the same Stensen who had written in Münster a treatise, *De Impositione Manuum*, concerning ordinations, ordainers and ordinands, which has done much to clarify the problems for others!

He even reproached himself on the score of non-performance of his duties as vicar apostolic—and this during the time when, as we know, he was consuming every ounce of his energy in Hanover and Münster. "As I await Rome's decision regarding my future," he wrote from Hamburg to Cosimo III in October, 1683, "I can think of only one thing both in relation to myself and my stay here. I reproach myself with having borne for six years the title of vicar apostolic to these countries and during all this time to have left everything for others to do and not to have visited these places myself. Today they are in such a state that should His Holiness give me nothing else to do, I could devote myself entirely to an attempt to restore pastoral care in the vicariates, and for that much time is needed."

He was awaiting from Rome the reply to a letter he had written to Pope Innocent on September 15, 1683. In this letter which gave further information regarding the spiritual situation in the Münster diocese, he had said he could not "before God exercise the functions of auxiliary bishop in such conditions and circumstances. . . . Consequently, I must with great sorrow implore Your Holiness to free me from this post as auxiliary bishop."

It is often said that Rome moves slowly, and our prelate was not impatient; he knew that the situation must be weighed carefully and prudently. To the Grand Duke of Tuscany he wrote: "I live in my customary state of detachment, praying

God for one grace alone, namely, to preserve me from offending Him. If He wishes to use me for some good, I confess my unworthiness, but He is the Lord. All that I ask is that He preserve me in His holy love."

On March 15, 1684, he wrote to the secretary of the Propaganda: "I learn from certain quarters that in Münster they wish me to return as auxiliary. I have no other desire than to do God's will and I believe He wants me there where His Holiness will send me." He goes on to say, however, that he had also learned that he would be received on condition he would promise to ordain, without making distinctions, all the candidates who would be sent to him. And he continues: "I received the episcopal dignity not for the purpose of becoming an auxiliary, but in order to serve in mission territory to convert others out of gratitude to God for having brought me into the Church. It seems to me therefore that God may wish me to end my days in the apostolic vicariates."

He then goes on to tell Bishop Cibo of his reaction to the offer of a benefice in Leghorn which he had received from Grand Duke Cosimo III: "Since Leghorn is a free port open to a variety of peoples who either reside there or pass through, it would be a fertile field for the conversion of souls. It would be a particular consolation to me if God would once more make use of me for a few years or days to accomplish some spiritual good for some of the Grand Duke's subjects or for other souls residing in Leghorn. But, as I fear this may be a hidden deception of my self-love, I dare not ask for this appointment from His Holiness or from God.

"But just as my love for my spiritual fatherland and my spiritual and temporal benefactors leads me to desire to render them service, so my love for my native country makes me desire for God to use me for the benefit of my compatriots. Then,

143

too, Hamburg is deserving of all my effort for the remainder of my days, for there is a great need for order in this mission to be restored. However in this, as in all other matters, I place myself in God's hands so that he may inspire His Holiness."

Rome's long-awaited reply was received in a letter written by Bishop Cibo on May 6, 1684, which stated that the Pope and the cardinals of the Congregation of the Propagation of the Faith valued Bishop Stensen's zeal so highly that they were unwilling to release him from the care of the vicariates. However, he was to make Hamburg his headquarters, and the apostolic vicariates placed under his jurisdiction would include the cities and dioceses of Halberstadt, Bremen, Magdeburg and Schwerin, and all places in the duchies of Mecklenburg, besides Hanover, Denmark and the Guelph countries.

Thus Bishop Stensen was finally released from the functions of auxiliary bishop of Münster which he had found so painful. However, the increase in his territories as vicar apostolic filled him with dread, "because I do not consider that I suffice for even one of them," he wrote Bishop Cibo. "Some of these places had never received one mark of attention from the vicar apostolic who was my predecessor.

"With regard to the promise of still other functions, Your Lordship knows I am ready to accept God's will. I would be made most happy to have you write me that I have been removed from all vicariates and other charges and left free to live in poverty as a simple priest."

In Hamburg, however, Bishop Stensen resided in the house of the Tuscan envoy, Theodor Kerckring. He was able to use the services of his courier and received substantial financial aid from Grand Duke Cosimo. This, together with the small stipend he received from the Holy See, enabled him to carry on his charitable activities. Even so, he had many causes for worry.

He had arrived in Hamburg in troubled times. Although, according to the provision of the Treaty of Westphalia, in the imperial cities there was religious parity, that is, equal rights for Catholics, Lutherans and Calvinists, the government and administration of Hamburg had fallen under the domination of the Lutheran ecclesiastical organization, and the attitude of its ministers led to frequent dissensions with the Catholics. These included native citizens as well as the representatives of the Catholic emperor, the king of France and the king of Spain; also the envoy of the Tuscan grand duke. Then, too, within the municipal government, there was a violent struggle for power between the well-to-do faction under Mayor Heinrich Meurer and the people's party under the merchant H. Snitger and the shipmaster Konrad Jastram.

"Merciful heavens," Stensen exclaimed, "what troubles we have here! The catastrophe of a great fire, internal dissensions in the city, threats from the imperial ministers, divisions among our ecclesiastics and the laity, and between laymen themselves. Finally the friends of the Jesuits are against me."

The conflagration referred to broke out on July 3 in the house of a shipbuilder through the carelessness of a pipe smoker. Some 2,000 housing units were reduced to ashes, and much misery ensued as well as troubles between opposing factions in the city. This was intensified by a quarrel between the municipal senate and the emperor's representative Von Rondeck.

As for Bishop Stensen's friends the Jesuits, this was a regrettable story which caused him mental anguish and in which he was called on to use tact and patience.

In Hamburg the Jesuits worked with much zeal and Bishop

145

Stensen saw and appreciated what they had done in the mission field. As we know, he had long since chosen his confessors from their ranks and followed their spiritual practices. He had even written to the Tuscan grand duke: "I would be happy if God would relieve me of the care of souls as vicar apostolic and allow me to die as a member of the Society."

After his arrival in Hamburg, there was dissension in the Jesuit community and he had occasion to inquire into the conduct of four missionaries against whom complaints had been made in Rome. Finding it advisable for the two oldest of the missionaries to be replaced, he wrote in succession to the three Jesuits who had been his confessors and to the provincial in Cologne. He asked that the two missionaries be recalled on the grounds of their age and lack of physical fitness for the missions and giving no other cause, in order to save them embarrassment and not to oblige the vicar apostolic to have formal recourse to Rome.

The provincial gave an unsatisfactory reply and unfortunately made the matter known to the community in Hamburg, so that the interested parties learned of the vicar apostolic's opinion and were incensed against him.

Without losing his calm, Bishop Stensen considered it his duty to write to the secretary of the Propaganda and to the general of the Society in Rome, Charles de Noyelle. The latter replied immediately in the most amiable terms, saying he had already done what was necessary and was sending two new missionaries to Hamburg.

However, the arrival of the new missionaries was delayed, and the two older men did not leave. When finally the oldest was recalled by the provincial and set out, he died on the way to Cologne. In a letter to the Hamburg community the provincial placed the responsibility for his recall on the shoulders of the vicar apostolic and feeling against the latter was further aroused.

After some months the new missionaries arrived but the departure of the second of the older men, Father Isaac, was delayed. Nothing was changed, and complaints against the vicar apostolic were sent to Rome. A petition was even made that he be removed, but no such action was taken.

At this point an incident occurred which placed another complexion on the matter. Father Isaac became embroiled in the political squabbles of the city because of his friendship for Mayor Meurer who was arrested and imprisoned by the municipal senate for betraying his decisions to the imperial representative, Von Rondeck. The Lutherans were greatly incensed and placed the blame at the door of the Jesuits.

Bishop Stensen was much distressed: "If the good Fathers had heeded my advice, and I am a faithful friend of their Society, this feeling against them would not have been aroused. For some time now I have asked that this missionary be replaced." And he added: "God alone knows why these complications have arisen. Yet we must bless Him always, because even when things appear a certain way to us, in His wisdom He knows better than we."

XI
Hamburg and Schwerin

BECAUSE OF HIS CLOSE ASSOCIATION with his friend and host Theodor Kerckring, Bishop Stensen found himself in the midst of other dissensions and clashes at the same time as the Jesuit affair. The Tuscan envoy was in the bad graces both of the imperial ambassador Dietrich von Rondeck and of Emperor Leopold I's special envoy, Count Anton von Berka. The vicar apostolic felt himself bound to side with Kerckring by special ties of justice and of gratitude—of justice because the accusations against Kerckring were completely groundless, and of gratitude because of the hospitality he had received over a period of many months.

148

The campaign against Kerckring had two causes. A handsome building was being constructed for the imperial embassy, with a chapel and quarters for the Jesuit missionaries. The imperial ambassador quarreled with the Jesuits and wanted them out of the picture under the pretext they had spent more for their quarters than the sum covered by the emperor's subsidy. Work was suspended, and the imperial representatives proposed that the partially completed building be sold and another, less costly, be bought in its stead. (Some suspected that Von Rondeck and Von Berka intended to pocket the difference.) Bishop Stensen sided with the Jesuits, fearing that the new plan would not include a place for worship, and it is thought it was he who caused Kerckring to intervene by sending correct information to the court in Vienna. In the meantime the Tuscan representative offered to pay the workmen to proceed, but they refused and demanded the wages already due them. All kinds of accusations were made against Kerckring, but the building was not sold. The two imperial representatives did not forgive their diplomatic colleague from Tuscany for his part in the affair.

The second cause of complaint against Kerckring was less complicated. A young woman, Anna von Kempe, the ward of the mayor of Hamburg, fell in love with a young man of good family and wished to marry him. Her guardian refused to give his consent because he hoped the young man would marry his own daughter. The betrothed couple appealed to the municipal senate, but not having received an answer at the end of eight months, decided to proceed with their wedding. The young man's brother, himself a member of the senate, offered his home for the ceremony; however, fearing some disagreeable incident might occur, he thought better of his offer and asked his friend Theodor Kerckring to allow him the use of

149

one of the rooms in his residence for a few hours. Kerckring gladly obliged him, and immediatetly a storm broke over his head. The senate drew up a complaint against the Tuscan envoy, factions formed on either side, and Count von Berka despatched a protest against Kerckring's conduct to the court at Vienna. This petty squabble between the envoys is said to have had its origin at a banquet when Kerckring, not realizing in what capacity Von Berka was present, failed to address him as "Your Excellency."

Bishop Stensen was saddened by these dissensions, especially as at this period he was going through one of his periods of depression and self-criticism in regard to the performance of his duties as vicar apostolic.

"Hamburg seems to have become a tower of Babel," he wrote, "so many are the divisions between men of every rank. Atheism is making progress, and I am scarcely able to describe the troubles that exist in this region. . . .

"My action is very limited. All places here where Catholics enjoy any degree of freedom are already provided by the Society of Jesus with a number of missionaries, so workers are not lacking. The result is I do not see a place for my services, since the superiors of the Society watch over their missions and make visitations to them.

"After a year of experience, I do not think it is advisable to have a vicar apostolic in a place where the Fathers of the Society are in charge. If they live according to the spirit of their Society, they have no need of a vicar apostolic to add his zeal to theirs; if, on the other hand, they do not follow in that spirit and fail to obey their superiors, a vicar apostolic cannot intervene without grave difficulties. . . .

"Here I am but the shadow of a vicar apostolic, and this increases my doubts as to whether I am doing God's will, since my presence and functions seem purposeless.

"To this is added the impossibility for a vicar apostolic to be able to live here without other revenues. God has given me a desire to live in true poverty, and has inspired the Grand Duke of Tuscany to give me alms so that I may support other poor people. I blush to think that within a year I have received from him 800 thalers, although I have taken little for myself and have used almost all for those in need of help."

In the year 1684, Bishop Stensen derived much consolation from a visit he received from a member of his family: "This year I had with me one of my nephews. Through a special favor of God he came to see me, and after a period of resistance to divine grace, he became a good Catholic.

"My sister also (in September of that same year) spent several days with me here on her way to Frankfort to care for her business interests. I found her still in the same spiritual state. She is pious in her own way, and she loves me, provided we do not speak of religion. If I broach this subject, she does not listen to me. . . . My sins and my coldness do not allow me to receive the grace to bring this soul into the path of salvation."

Our prelate was still obsessed by the idea of his own unworthiness. The failings of others he attributed to his ignorance, lukewarmness and negligence. At the same time he was in fact very active, carrying out a thousand duties in connection with his ministry. He preached often, traveled over his mission territories and engaged in written controversy with certain Protestant theologians. Often he made conversions and afterward found employment for those he had brought into

151

the Catholic Church. He sought out those who had gone astray, took care of great numbers of the poor and of others in moral distress.

For instance there was the renegade Italian Franciscan, Antonio Nepeta, who had embraced the Lutheranism of the woman he married, and who was practicing the profession of physician. Bishop Stensen spent much effort trying to help the unfortunate man, who had one time seemed to repent his apostasy, and met Nepeta's atheistic and rationalistic arguments by making a heart dissection for his benefit: "I showed him the wonderful structure of the heart in order to make more obvious the wisdom of God in its functioning." He also wrote for Nepeta an epistle—*Experimenta naturalia ad Sacrae Scripturae* —to convince him of the conformity between nature and the teachings of the Bible. Bishop Stensen's prolonged efforts seem to have been of no avail, although he wrote to Rome and Florence on Nepeta's behalf and had prayers said for him. Finally, he came to the conclusion: "Nepeta's deplorable state of soul causes me great sorrow; in truth he seems abandoned by God."

Meanwhile, during the autumn of 1684, Bishop Stensen concluded a debate which had started more than ten years earlier while he was royal anatomist at Copenhagen (prior to his becoming a priest). His opponent was a very important Lutheran theologian, Johan Brunsmand. Bishop Stensen now sent him his already published apologetic treatises and, when Brunsmand declared himself unconvinced, the bishop in a letter of December 9, 1684, requested proof of a single error in the Catholic doctrine. Once more he pointed out that individual Bible interpretation was not enough and that only the teaching of the Church could lead to certainty.

Around this time Bishop Stensen also felt it his duty to make reply to an outburst of Jansenism which had taken root in several places and was professed not only by certain priests but also several bishops. As early as July 1677, when he was in Rome, he had taken his position against this doctrine in an attack on the book of P. Noris, a French ex-priest. At that time Stensen wrote: "In matters regarding the purity of the faith, it is impossible to be too careful." It seems the book had now been translated into German and was being taken very seriously in certain quarters.

In Hamburg, Bishop Stensen lived in better circumstances than in either Hanover or Münster, since he enjoyed the hospitality of the Tuscan envoy. In Theodor Kerckring he found a true friend, a generous protector, a zealous Catholic, a man of learning and intelligence. The vicar apostolic officiated always in the chapel of Kerckring's residence and was provided with every convenience. In a letter of February 16, 1684, to Cosimo III he had written: "I recognize God's paternal care in giving me this place of refuge during this unusually cold winter. Here I can enjoy the warmth of an excellent stove . . . which is more than I had at Münster. It seems that God treats me as a little child. May it please His divine goodness to allow me to derive from this the strength I shall need to sustain me on those days I must bear the Cross and when vigor is needed."

To the same prince he wrote on October 8, 1685: "For two years I have enjoyed here with Your Highness' minister every comfort I could desire. Besides having me at his table, he has allowed me the use of a house opposite for my exclusive use, without accepting any return for its various expenses."

Bishop Stensen was still dissatisfied with the manner he was carrying out his obligations. In February, 1685, he had written to the Grand Duke of Florence: "I must consider how I may free myself from duties with the performance of which I am not satisfied." After much endeavor on his part, it seemed to him he had accomplished nothing. He hesitated to make a decision. There were three possibilities open to him should he resign his vicariates: to retire to a secluded place for several years to engage in his theological writings in answer to Brunsmand's attacks on Catholic doctrines; to remain in Hamburg as a simple missionary and chaplain of the Tuscan embassy; or to live at Leghorn "not as a prelate but having in charge a benefice, and in association with other priests who wished to live in community."

Since the Tuscan grand duke had again invited him to come to Leghorn, he requested the Congregation of the Propaganda for authorization to go to Rome in order to explain in person the situation in his vicariates and to see how it might be regularized. The reply was in the negative, the Propaganda deeming it inexpedient for him to undertake the fatigue of a long voyage when he might explain in writing the administrative difficulties in the territories in his charge.

He thereupon sent to Pope Innocent XI a detailed report in which are evident his perspicacity and practical sense as well as his zeal. He concluded: "I find myself superfluous in this country, and am moreover a burden to His Highness of Tuscany, who has shown me so many other favors. He now offers me an opportunity to live at Leghorn where I can devote myself to a spiritual life and the continuation of my studies. There I could also meet non-Catholics who pour in from various countries. I humbly implore Your Holiness for permission to spend several years there. I could in this way finish my reply to a Lutheran book which my countrymen regard as very important and at least in this regard show them the concern I feel for the salvation of their souls."

An unforeseen incident now occurred to delay the further-

154

ance of his plans. He learned from some Mecklenburg noble-
men who had been converted to Catholicism that conditions
had become such that Catholic worship could be held in
Schwerin in virtue of the articles of the Westphalia agreement.
However, in order for such services to be assured of continuity,
they should be held in a private residence at the expense of
the Catholics rather than in the palace of Duke Christian
Louis of Mecklenburg who was childless and most probably
would have a Protestant successor.

Bishop Stensen informed the Congregation of the Propaganda of this development, stating that if the Pope should
grant his request to retire to Leghorn for a time he could
stop in Paris on his way to Italy and see the Duke of Mecklenburg, who spent the greater part of each year in the French
capital. An understanding might be reached which could be
discussed in Rome on Stensen's arrival.

This time to his great joy he received an affirmative answer,
and began making his plans, his itinerary and his preparations:
"I seek no material advantages," he said. "I am content with
very little and I do not think I am mistaken in believing I
can live even in a state of beggary. But truly I have great need
of a spiritual retreat, not only of eight days but of several
months. In this way I can find myself again after all these
years of constant distractions. I hope God will grant me that
favor in my true fatherland where I began my life in the
Church."

Because Bishop Stensen still had members of his family in
Denmark, before leaving for Italy he made a hurried journey
to Copenhagen to see his sister Anna, his nephews and his
friends. There he passed some ten days with his relatives and
during this time was able discreetly to confer the sacrament

155

of Confirmation on certain Danish Catholics, something which had not been possible since the time of Luther.

Back in Hamburg on September 13, 1685, Bishop Stensen was faced with a new development. He tells us: "On my return, as I was thinking of setting out on my journey to Italy, I received from his Serene Highness of Mecklenburg his personal authorization to live in Schwerin and freely to conduct services in the ducal chapel. Actually what I had tried to obtain was permission for his subjects to set up a chapel in a private house, so that in case of the Duke's death, worship would remain free and in accord with the Münster (Westphalia) settlement. It seems that, due to private agreements he had made with members of his family, His Highness could not grant this permission, and that his Catholic subjects will themselves have to persuade his brothers to allow it. In any case I must go to see conditions at first hand, confer with the Catholics of the region, and see how matters may be arranged. This obliges me to delay my journey for another few weeks and perhaps even for the winter.

"I scarcely know what God's will is for me. It seems He wants me always to go about blindly, living from day to day for months at a time. Yet I recognize and bless His will in all things, since what He permits is only just because of our sins. . . . Often in the ways of God we discover divine providence in matters that are least apparent in human eyes."

On October 9, 1685, he wrote Cosimo III. "Last evening just as I had everything ready to start out this morning (for Schwerin), I learned that the Jesuit who conducts the French services here in Hamburg must leave this morning for Copenhagen. I must therefore remain for several days until he is replaced, since there is no one else to hear the confessions of persons who speak only French."

156

The new priest did not arrive until the first days of December, and in the meantime a wave of anti-Catholic feeling broke out in Hamburg as news was received that the French king, Louis XIV, had revoked the edict of Nantes, and had prohibited Protestant instruction and worship in his country. The wildest rumors were spread in Hamburg against the Catholics, against the Jesuits, and against the vicar apostolic. "The people are so agitated," Stensen wrote, "that various persons have warned us to be careful. There is much ill will against Mr. Kerckring because he protects me in his residence. Even so, I do not believe that for several centuries the Catholic Church has had such success here as during the past few months." This was no doubt one of the causes of the resentment.

It was only on the 11th of December that Bishop Stensen was able to leave Hamburg on the Lübeck mail coach. He arrived in Schwerin three days later to find his presence greatly needed. The only priest there, Father Jacob Steffani, an Augustinian, was in ill health and out of favor at the ducal court. The vicar apostolic quickly discovered that the Catholics in Schwerin were very few in number and their spiritual needs were great. On December 22, he wrote: "I have very little hope of opening a place of worship here. The duke is still abroad and seems to take very slight interest in religious matters. At least, with God's help, I will remain for the approaching feasts."

He did not know it, but he was destined never to leave.

Because Father Steffani was ill, he conducted services in the ducal chapel but he "thought it wiser not to appear as a bishop but as a simple missionary priest." He said: "Although I do not see where this will end, my presence seems necessary to put things in better order for the spiritual welfare of the few Catholics here."

Indeed he found things in an unfortunate state: "Mixed marriages, divisions of faith in the upbringing of the children of the same family, all attending the Lutheran school where the teaching of the Lutheran catechism is enforced, the parents working on Catholic feasts, eating meat on fastdays, and a lack of any scruple in other matters of this kind."

While he remained in Schwerin in an effort to remedy the situation, Bishop Stensen followed developments in Hamburg, and went back there at one point to bless the holy oils on Holy Thursday, April 10, 1686. He learned of new anti-Catholic demonstrations in the city: "The Lutherans," he wrote to Grand Duke Cosimo on May 25, "are still exasperated against our people and hurl insults at them in the streets. The rumor is spread that Your Serene Highness sends me money to make men papists, as they express it. Twice a week the mail arrives from France and each time it causes new disturbances. May it please God to arrange matters in that country (France) so that He is not continually offended by the sacrilege of those who receive the sacraments without faith. Whatever might be said about treating with severity those Catholics who apostatize, or born heretics who use violence against Catholics, it seems to me inexcusable to force people to profess a religion and approach sacraments in which they do not believe—*Faith is the gift of God.*"

During his stay in Schwerin, Bishop Stensen often asked the Apostle's question: "Lord, what would you have me do?" Many times his letters written during this period show him undecided as to his course.

He was asked by the prince bishop of Trier to come to him

158

as his auxiliary. But above all else he feared the prospect of ordaining unworthy candidates to the priesthood, and he still hoped to carry out his plans for Italy. Finally persuaded that it would be impossible to establish a Catholic chapel in Schwerin on any durable basis, and that some other missionary could carry out the work he was doing there, he wrote to Pope Innocent XI assuring him that he was willing to go wherever he might direct.

In a letter, under date of August 3, to Cosimo he said: "I am placing in the hands of His Holiness the decision as to whether to remain in the vicariates or to go to Trier—but not as auxiliary bishop, for that I dread. However God might wish to use me in some mission in the territories of that electorate, where Father Sterck tells me non-Catholics are quite numerous."

He sent his request for instructions to the Pope on August 1, but at the end of November he had still received no reply. "God knows," he wrote to Bishop Cibo, secretary of the Propaganda, "why the answer is so delayed. . . . I will wait with obedience and humility until God may see fit to let me know His commands."

However, the reply could have been received without changing the situation, for his departure would in any case have been postponed. In the middle of October, Father Steffani, the only priest in Schwerin, became very ill and took to his bed. For five weeks Bishop Stensen nursed him with tender and loving care. On November 22, Father Steffani died.

XII

Testimonies

THE MANNER in which Stensen spent the last years of his life
is known to us from the writings of two members of his household. The first is Caspar Engelbert Schmael, who passed five
years with Bishop Stensen, first as a seminarian and later as
his curate in Hamburg. The other is Johann Rosen, a Swede
by birth and a captain in the army of the Duke of Hanover.
Rosen became a Catholic in 1678, and abandoning his military
career, was preparing to become a priest. He spent the winter
of 1685 in Schwerin with the vicar apostolic, to whom he
was greatly devoted. The testimony of these two witnesses

160

confirms all that has been said here of Niels Stensen's zeal and piety.

To priests the bishop said: "When the mothers of Bethlehem saw their little children put to the sword by Herod's soldiers, they could not be consoled. How can a pastor be consoled when he sees souls he should be preparing for heaven in danger of being lost? . . . The fig tree was allowed for a time to stand, but when it produced nothing, it was cut down. The same is true of priests who bring forth no good fruit. Do not think these are the thoughts of a scrupulous person. You are of the chosen line, and there is no middle course open to you—either you strive for the crown God has prepared for you, or you must expect the consequences."

In regard to conversation, Bishop Stensen gave the following advice:

"Speak little, only on certain subjects, and not about yourself. Live within yourself and take care of your own affairs.

"Pray God to make you affable in conversations with your neighbor. Do not allow peace and union among brothers to be disrupted by your words, even when they might appear to be demanded by zeal for perfection, because all other virtues give way before charity.

"Tell only what is quite certain, when charity requires it and when the listener is giving you his attention. Also, think first and speak afterward.

"Say what is adapted to the capacity of your listener, so that his mind can grasp what you have to say.

"Let your conversations be brief and spiritual and fortified by prayer.

"Avoid undue familiarity, hurried words, much laughter, bodily contacts, gestures and glances. Avoid all presumptuous words and gestures, oaths and lies.

161

"Above all avoid speaking ill of anyone. . . . We might do worse ourselves if God did not help us."

Stensen was the first to put his counsels into practice, as Johann Rosen testifies: "I can say that his conversation was always saintly and agreeable. He knew how to turn any conversation, on no matter what subject, to God's glory and the good of souls. Very often he would turn these conversations to the three stages of the spiritual life—the purgative, the illuminative and the unitive; he would show the ways in which souls come to union with God through love. I dare to say—and I base this on what was visible and on what I came to know of his interior dispositions over the long period I lived with the Bishop—that his recollection and union with God were almost continual and on a very high plane. When he discussed such questions he did so with grace and ease, with joy and enthusiasm. Even non-Catholics delighted in listening to him, and not rarely became his converts."

Francesco Redi and Lorenzo Magalotti, Stensen's friends of the Cimento circle in Florence, also spoke of the charm of his conversation.

In his definition of a humble man Stensen was really describing himself:

"The humble man, knowing himself unworthy of esteem and deserving of contempt, scorns himself in his own eyes and heart. He desires and even rejoices to be treated in this manner by others, accepting such things, should they come, for the glory of God. . . .

"Knowing that without grace he can do nothing in God's service, and warned by the fall of other men of the risks he runs, he mistrusts his mental workings, his judgment and his

162

abilities. In cases where there is danger of committing sin, he undertakes nothing without full deliberation. For a man to trust in God and place his hope solely in Him is to lift himself up. All strength lies in humility, and only the proud man is weak.

"The humble man says nothing about himself, and makes no allusion to what good he may have accomplished or what he may have been to the end of arousing admiration in others. He is careful to hide his natural gifts in order to preserve them and also because God alone should be praised.

"He is a man of few words, and those words are wise. He chooses what is less desirable in the way of lodging, clothing, food and position. To arrive at true humility, he likes to talk with poor and simple men—these bear the mark of the sons of God and are His living images. St. Louis, the king of France, each week washed the feet of the poor and served them at table.

"The humble man distrusts no one; he says nothing against anybody; he has a good opinion of all. In so far as he can, he excuses the faults of others; he treats everyone with affability and kindness and with the honor due to each."

Father Schmael tells us: "He truly lived in this manner. He was so humble he made himself the servant of one and all. He often visited the sick and took them the sacraments. At Schwerin his behavior was that of a simple priest; several times when I visited him he acted as my server at Mass as though he were a seminarian. His conversation was simple and frank and I never heard an un-Christian word pass his lips. The Lutheran gentlemen of all ranks who visited him openly said his way of life resembled that of the bishops of the early Church. He was prudent and constant in his practice of charity; neither pleas nor threats could turn him aside from a good deed. And it is impossible to praise too highly his unalterable chastity and incredible patience."

Just as Bishop Stensen described humility, he also described poverty at first hand:

"He lives in poverty who possesses nothing of his own, and he considers as alms bestowed on him those necessary things he uses, such as his clothing and his breviary; he thinks of God as his sole inheritance and possession. He accepts no emolument, and if such are attached to his office he takes from them only what is actually sufficient for a poor man to live; if his superiors permit, he distributes the rest to others and goes about like a beggar.

"When his health allows, he travels only on foot or by boat; or, if he does not have the strength to do this, he uses the poorest means of transportation. If he happens to have money for his journey, he distributes it among the poor. In places where there is a hospice for the poor or a hospital, he does not go to an inn. He takes as little food and drink as possible. He uses a little straw and a poor covering for his bed.

"He is poor who lives only on what is necessary, recognizes that it comes from a bounteous God, and thanks Him for what he owes Him; even the use of those spiritual goods he asks from God he regards as alms. A beggar does not eat in the manner and at the time he might wish, but when food is given to him; he asks frequently, but is not often heard; nevertheless, if he receives what is necessary and sometimes even more, he divides it with the poor who are his fellows. We should do the same by not trying to decide anything in regard to our future in accordance with our own wishes, but leaving it to others to obtain what we desire. Thus, like the beggar, we will be satisfied with what we receive, and if we do not receive it, we will also be content. . . . To conclude: in spiritual matters we should not torment ourselves as to whether we understand this or that and about the way we carry things out, but should say to ourselves: I will have and I will do what God wishes, and in the manner and at the time determined by Him."

According to Schmael: "Stensen practiced the poverty of a hermit. During the five years I lived with him he never slept on a bed, but either on a bench or the floor and using an old cloak as his covering. He went to bed very late, and rose very early."

Rosen gives the following details: "When he was at Hanover and Münster, his household rose at five o'clock. A half hour later they gathered for prayers and Bishop Stensen read them several passages from the *Imitation of Christ*, a little work he greatly admired and always carried around with him. After prayers all went to the Mass which he celebrated every day except the last two days of his life; he even said Mass on days when he was painfully ill. (Sometimes I saw him singing Mass when he was tortured with terrific pain from a stomach ailment which chronically afflicted him.) In the afternoon we all made a visit to the Blessed Sacrament; in the evening after dinner, there were examination of conscience and more prayers. His house could have been considered the model for a monastery.

"When he was at Hamburg he did not wish anyone to wait on him, and I found him in a pitiable state on my return from Paris. Pale and emaciated, with sunken eyes, he had deprived himself of every comfort; nevertheless he was happy and the look on his face inspired reverence. He was dressed as a poor man, wrapped in an old cloak which he wore at all

165

seasons and especially in winter when he made the greater number of his missionary visitations, going about from one place to another in rain and snow. He suffered greatly from the cold, but never wanted to wear an extra coat or gloves. He had a certain way of concealing his misery, so that no one would pity or sympathize with him.

"Although he had only a very small stipend as vicar apostolic, he found means to help a number of Catholics among the new converts. He left everything to Providence, and Providence always came to his aid by inspiring others—and especially the Grand Duke of Florence—to supply him with abundant funds for alms. When the charity of others did not equal his own, he gave away whatever he had in his house. One day when he had nothing else for the poor, he gave away his episcopal ring and pectoral cross."

For his part, Father Schmael states: "His wardrobe was restricted to the bare minimum: three sackcloth shirts, three clerical collars, a threadbare black soutane, a poor biretta, and a few miserable undergarments. But the greatest evidence of his penitential spirit was the treatment he inflicted on his body. He always fasted on Mondays, Wednesdays and Saturdays, taking in the evening only a little dry bread and a glass of beer. He never deviated from this program even when he had walked all day and was exhausted from fatigue. During the last three years of his life, he took no wine at table, and ate neither fresh meat nor fish. When he had some important duty before him, such as ordinations or pastoral visitations, he ate practically no food for three days. I alone knew this, for he ordered me to give away secretly to the poor the food prepared for him. On those days of fast, he would invite certain of the poor to dine; he served the table himself, read

166

to them from a devotional work and sent them away with alms."

To this life of austerity and mortification, Stensen added other penitential practices. His household became alarmed and begged him to lessen his austerities. Father Sterck especially wrote to him at length, telling him he was endangering his health and thus reducing the amount of good he could accomplish.

Stensen replied simply: "It is obvious God wants me to live this way, because it does not cause me to lose either strength or health."

XIII

His Spiritual Writings

STENSEN'S FRIENDS in Florence considered him very learned, giving the word a more extensive meaning than it has today. He was not only a great scientist and a saintly ecclesiastic, but also a prolific writer as may be seen from the six large volumes of his published works.

We have gone into some detail concerning his scientific treatises. In these he very clearly describes the most difficult matters in Latin, a language often lacking the vocabulary for hitherto unexplained subjects. He wrote only of what he himself had observed in the course of his experiments and observations, stating facts that he had verified several times. After sin, there was nothing he detested so much as ill-grounded conclusions, paradoxical expressions, braggadocio, or obscure terminology.

Especially after his conversion he understood the limitations of human intelligence and abilities. To a friend who was ill he wrote: "May God be the One to restore you to perfect health, for we see our own art to be very imperfect." On another occasion he wrote to the same friend: "If our natural faculties are composed of marvelous and almost incomprehensible elements, how much more marvelous are the elements of grace which enable the soul to attain to God and His mysteries.

"I have friends in Holland who completely accept the Cartesian philosophy, even to the point of making this philosophy the judge of the meaning and nature of grace. At the present time, I am seeking by means of this philosophy itself to demonstrate that natural intelligence throws no more light on the subject of grace than a blind man's touch may be compared to what we see. I am trying to probe the weaknesses of this philosophy to establish what can be determined by it in regard to natural things, what it cannot determine, and why this is.

"As you are interested in the natural sciences, I beg you to be kind enough to continue on your side to seek what can be proved and what cannot be proved by natural means. In this way with God's help we may serve to bring minds back to Christian humility and complete submission to His Word."

Stensen's gift for observation was highly developed. Unfortunately most of the notebooks in which he put down memoranda for his personal use have been lost. He noted

169

even things which might appear insignificant to us; but he was trying to get down to causes through the study of effects. For instance, he saw a drop of water on the limb of a tree; the limb was slightly shaken and the drop of water fell to the ground. Why did it happen? (This was shortly prior to Newton's statement of the law of gravitation.) Stensen studied the reason why some metals liquefy easily while others take much more time—what prevented liquefaction and what provoked it?

Elsewhere he noted: "Particles of snow or a thin layer of ice on my window sill rapidly disappear. They do not leave any trace of humidity." And further on: "We take something that has had perfume put on it; we weigh it, and put it aside until the smell has disappeared. Then we weigh it again to see if there is any difference in the weight."

One evening he notes that he had spent all day in study, and after dinner had made an experiment which was successful only in part. From this, his thoughts took wing: "I should never be troubled by any accident; I should never be irritated by insults to me or to my friends; I should not allow misfortune to distress me. God foresees and provides for all things, and I should see them in relation to Him and His glory." Then, without interruption, he notes: "When flocks of storks fly over the Mediterranean, they become exhausted and fall in great numbers on the passing ships. See if we can find out from someone where they live in winter."

It remains for us to glance at his theological writings and his correspondence. The first are collected in two large folio volumes, one containing apologetic and polemical treatises, the other his spiritual works, sermons and religious tracts.

Our first impression is of how quickly the great anatomist acquired a mastery of the terminology used by a Church with whose doctrine he was unfamiliar and which he distrusted for many years. Soon he knew that doctrine well; he was the faithful exponent not only of the Church's teachings but of its idiom.

In contrast to many of the preachers of his time who do not seem to have heard of the existence of the Fathers of the Church, he drew copiously from their writings as also from Holy Scripture. It is surprising he had time to make so deep a study of these sources, and that his memory retained so much scriptural and patristic matter.

The major part of the second volume of his theological works is made up of forty-five sermons or homilies he preached on feastdays, Sundays and other occasions. Solid in substance, they contain food for thought and inspiration to virtue, and in them the orator's missionary zeal and the richness of his own spiritual life are evident. These sermons contain many praises of the Blessed Virgin, whose feasts during the year gave Stensen occasion to make meditations on her virtues and prerogatives, and to urge others to love and imitate her. He also had a great veneration for St. Joseph, saying: "The Blessed Virgin would be offended if we placed another saint before Joseph," and he often invoked the foster father of Our Lord for the grace of a happy death. We do not know what other saints Stensen chose as his patrons. He mentions many saints, but among his favorites were Charles Borromeo, whom he often referred to, and Francis de Sales whose practices and manner he tried to imitate.

In all these sermons—which, were they to be translated from the Latin, could stand as models for sermons today—we see Stensen's complete orthodoxy and fidelity to the thought and spirit of the Church and his respect and obedience to the See of Peter. In one sermon he says: "A human mind in a

171

human body cannot even understand the nature of the soul. It is certain the soul exists and operates, but what it is and how it operates we do not know. And yet men are presumptuous enough to try to understand all these matters without a teacher to guide them. . . . If you are a member of the flock, listen to your Shepherd; if you are her child, ask for food from your Mother the Church, that is, from Christ."

There is much more good material in this second volume. We have already referred to Stensen's advice to pastors, *Parochorum hoc age.* We might glance at his *Opera spirituale,* written when he was in Florence and in Italian, a book he carried with him to Germany and reread as a guide for his actions.

It begins as follows: "There are no other means to enjoy even human happiness on this earth than those taught by Our Lord. These teachings may be summed up as always to live in God's presence, to rid oneself of bad habits and each day to make thanksgiving to God. As soon as you rise, begin to pray. Adore the Holy Trinity in the most perfect way at your command, for this devotion is superior to any other, and all others should be added to it. Devotion to the Blessed Trinity is a great sign of sanctity."

Farther on, we find this advice: "In thoughts, words and actions seek every imaginable means at every time and on every occasion to please the Invisible who guards you as a Father and is the Author of all good things; do this for Him out of respect and love."

Elsewhere: "Love no other than Him and through Him. Let nothing distress you save only what offends Him. Desire nothing but to see Him and to do His holy will. Trust only in His goodness . . . place your confidence in His wisdom and loving providence."

172

If after the *Opera spirituale*, we examine the tracts in which he discusses humility and the other virtues, deals with the contemplative life and the sufferings of the Cross, we realize we are in the presence of a man of great sanctity. This, of course, is our personal impression and in saying this we do not pretend to anticipate the judgment of the Church.

However, we are not the only one to share this impression. Father Gustav Scherz (who has since given us an account of Stensen's life and work and especially of his scientific labors in *Nicolaus Steno and His Indice*, Copenhagen, 1958) also published in Copenhagen a pamphlet containing testimonies to Stensen's holiness rendered by a number of well-known personages. Such testimonies were very numerous at the time the scientist-bishop lived; afterward, due to circumstances, they became less frequent, but nevertheless they continued to be made.

At the beginning of his pamphlet, Father Scherz places a letter written on February 29, 1953, by Pope Pius XII, in which the Pontiff states: "Through his pursuit of truth and his admirable life, Niels Stensen was a man who acquired great merits; his magnificent example was truly a lamp for the men of his time and for those of our own day. He regarded it as a sacred duty to preserve the Catholic faith intact and to fight in Christ's cause. He surmounted grave difficulties with inflexible firmness and in full submission to the Church, having but one aim in view: the greater glory of God and the good of souls."

Pius XII himself had great veneration for this illustrious son of Denmark and of the Church. In a radio message to Danish Catholics, in May 1953, the Pontiff recalled this famous figure in their national history in these words: "Let us also remember those who at the time of sad separation and

173

during the centuries that followed struggled in the behalf of the Catholic Church. One of these should be mentioned here by name: Niels Stensen of whom you are justly proud. He was great as a scientist and great because of his unreserved devotion to the Missions of the North."

It is told that through the intercession of the saintly bishop favors have been obtained by persons in Denmark and northern Germany where he worked as vicar apostolic. A publication of the Holy See informs us that inquiries preparatory to the introduction of the cause of his beatification have been made in the dioceses of Osnabrück and Paderborn.

Stensen's correspondence is published in two large volumes containing together 1,027 pages. Their perusal is rewarding for it takes the reader all over Europe at a most interesting period in history; we meet new people on every page and learn a great deal about some of them. A thousand events of the times are described, and in Stensen's company the reader shares the interests of a fresh and inquiring mind.

Even to those he knew best, he did not betray a word of disillusionment or deception at having put aside his career and the honors that came to him as a scientist. Yet this renunciation must have required almost superhuman effort on the part of one so passionately interested in scientific research. Once ordained a priest, he lived for God alone, in an effort to save souls and to assuage the moral and bodily ills of his fellows.

He writes: "God is truly glorified when, out of love for Him, we energetically carry out those things most opposed to our exterior nature. This pleases God so much that Holy Scripture tells us it is the way he opens before His dearest

174

friends, giving them the occasions to practice great mortifications and at the time granting them help to do so.

"The truth is that God seems deliberately to prepare the most difficult things for his friends, so that in carrying them out they may manifest to the world His wisdom, power and glory.

"The cause of all the ills suffered by Catholicism seems to me to be that its children have not sufficiently understood the necessity of suffering. Also I am not certain that if persecution of the Church were to cease it would be a great blessing. . . . It is said that faith spreads in times of peace. I believe this insofar as it affects the number of Christians on earth, but I also believe that more went to heaven in the days of Domitian and of other persecutors of the Church."

The personage to whom Stensen wrote most often was the Grand Duke of Tuscany. "After God, I can think of nothing in the world more holy than true friendship." The letters also confirm us in the belief that the discredited Cosimo III had himself some excellent qualities. Even with this benefactor, however, the prelate did not forget he was a priest of God. With his habitual courtesy and charity, he often took advantage of the feast of some saint or other occasion to give him spiritual advice, as the following examples will show:

"May St. Charles Borromeo, whose feast we celebrate today, reward your devotion to him by giving you the grace to use all your time, all the forces of your mind, and all occasions for the good of souls who have been placed under the rule of Your Serene Highness."

Or again: "Today is the feast of St. Andrew who so much loved the Cross. May the same divine light that enlightened his mind make us understand the need of the Cross in expiation

175

of our sins. . . . May God grant Your Serene Highness and all the members of your household as well as myself, the most unworthy of men, the grace of losing none of the merit of our tribulations."

Here are some of the precepts which Bishop Stensen set down for others toward the end of his life:

"A Paradise is composed of the will of God; always conform yourself to it. Even if the world seems askew and falling about your head, do not be troubled. Turn to God with confidence in his goodness.

"Never be satisfied or stop doing the things of God; infinite goodness can never be sufficiently served.

"When you suffer pains of body or soul, offer them to the Divine Majesty in union with Christ's passion and in satisfaction for your sins.

"It is not only when the sea is tossed by storms but even when it is ruffled by a slight breeze that it is less apt to reflect the heavens over it; in the same way it is not only when the soul is troubled by mortal sin but when it is disturbed by small ambitions that it is less likely to reflect the image of God.

"Love is not perfect when we love only those who love us. God loves those who do not love Him and even those who hate Him.

"Insofar as possible, try to combine the things of God with the things of the world, so that you may induce men of the world to follow God.

"All the honey of the world is not so sweet as the gall of Christ.

"Ask God for temporal things only for the day that is present. If He gives no more, render Him thanks; and, for your part, if you have what is needed for one day, be satisfied and have no care for tomorrow.

176

"If in this life you spend your time in acquiring superficial knowledge, friends and honors, at the hour of death you will find yourself stripped of everything. So try to acquire what cannot be taken away, and fill your soul only with such things as are pleasing to God.

"Patience does not consist in not feeling pain—that is not in our power. Rather it exists in praising God as though we were in bliss.

"The death of the just is a happy passage from the light of earth into the light that is divine, the exchange of passing satisfactions for eternal happiness, and at the end, instead of finding gifts, finding the Giver. It is true much is lost, but what is acquired in its place is very great."

In Niels Stensen's own case these words were prophetic.

XIV

The Last Chapter

IT COULD HAVE BEEN FORESEEN that Bishop Stensen's exhausting labors and great austerities would bring him prematurely to the grave. He had long suffered from a chronic stomach ailment, and was frequently in the grip of severe pain. Even at such times he never failed to say Mass; he often preached several times a day, and continued to expend his strength for the spiritual and material welfare of his flock.

On November 21, 1686 (corresponding to December 1, according to the Gregorian calendar reform of 1585, which had not yet been adopted in the countries of Northern Europe),

178

Stensen suffered a painful attack of his ailment. Despite his suffering, he insisted on going to the ducal chapel, especially since it was Sunday. There he celebrated Mass and gave a sermon in French, returning again in the afternoon to hold vespers and compline and to preach in German.

That night he was unable to sleep and was in continual pain. Nevertheless, next day he went to the chapel to say Mass and preach a sermon in honor of St. Cecilia, whose feast it was. The signs of his sufferings were plainly visible on his face and several times he seemed on the verge of fainting.

Afterward he confessed to Johann Rosen, who accompanied him, that he did not feel well and could not account for his indisposition. Rosen told the bishop that he was making too much demand on his strength and reminded him of his long vigils at the bedside of Father Steffani.

"No," Bishop Stensen replied, "it is my old trouble. Let God do what He wills."

He could take no food, but refused to undress and rested in a chair. That night he slept on the floor. On Tuesday morning he again wished to go to the chapel to say Mass, but was dissuaded by Rosen who finally convinced him that a physician should be called.

After making an examination, the doctor left the room. To those waiting outside he said: "His life has been too austere," and shook his head.

When these words were repeated to him, Stensen replied: "If my penances have hastened my death, it does not distress me. I did these things with the intention of pleasing God. Others have lived on bread and water as I have done, even taking less and over longer periods of time. There is no reason for not continuing to follow their example if God wishes me to remain in the world."

179

On Wednesday he allowed his household to prepare a bed for him, by which time his abdomen had swelled noticeably. Despite intense suffering, he made no word of complaint, but prayed continually, often repeating the words: "Jesus, be my Saviour!"

His greatest trial was not to receive the sacraments, for after the death of Father Steffani, the curate of the Duke of Mecklenburg, no priest remained in the region. A message was despatched to a Jesuit who was stationed at Lübeck, but little hope was held that he might arrive in time. The sick bishop made public confession and an act of contrition before a group of people who had gathered at his bedside. Both Catholics and Protestants were among them, for during his stay in Schwerin he had come to be greatly admired.

After confessing his shortcomings and begging the pardon of everyone for any offenses he might have committed against them, he said: "I thank you, Lord, for your infinite mercy in calling me into the Catholic Church. . . . It is a great sorrow to me to be deprived of the last sacraments. I declare to all that I die in the Catholic Christian faith and in full submission to the holy Catholic Church."

All present were greatly moved, but he would allow no expressions of sympathy. He now knew his end was near and told those about him he wished to be buried in the plainest manner, and he appointed the faithful Rosen as his sole heir. This legacy was very small, for it consisted of Stensen's few poor garments and some books, his manuscripts on theological and spiritual subjects, and a red purse in which he carried his two pontifical rings and a pectoral cross containing, among others, the relics of St. Ignatius Loyola, St. Francis Xavier, and St. Philip Neri. In addition to these things, he left debts amounting to 200 thalers which he had borrowed to give to the poor—a debt afterward paid by Cosimo III.

On Wednesday, the day before he died, he wrote two letters to the grand duke. One was to be sent immediately upon his demise; the second, recommending to his care Rosen and a young nephew who was with him at Schwerin, was to be carried by them to Florence.

The first letter began: "This will probably be the last time Your Highness will see my handwriting, for it has pleased God to send me a sickness and sufferings which I believe are bringing my life to an end." After describing his symptoms, he said: "In the meantime, in the interests of justice, and as Your Serene Highness gave me permission, I borrowed from Mr. Kerckring 200 thalers which I still owe. And if I should die, I hope Your Serene Highness will bear the necessary expenses of my funeral which I desire to be very simple."

He recommended to the grand duke's generosity four friends: Johann Rosen and his nephew, the boy's tutor Pilgram, and a student of theology who lived with them. Then he continued: "I beg God on behalf of Your Serene Highness the blessing of a good life for yourself, for your household, and for the country over which you rule. . . . Again, on behalf of my spiritual sons I beg of you funds for their journey to Florence, and for the boy to continue his studies with his uncle (Rosen) and his tutor Pilgram, under direction of the Fathers of the Society of Jesus. Do not allow him to go to the court before he is firmly anchored in the Christian way of life, for not many pages and young courtiers are concerned about their salvation. I beg this charity of Your Serene Highness as I am dying."

Rosen's nephew was a boy of twelve. His father, who had

181

become a Catholic in opposition to the wishes of his wife, had entrusted the lad to Rosen's care and that of Bishop Stensen, in order to remove him from the mother's influence. The boy was unhappy away from home, and desperately anxious to return. However, when he saw the saintly bishop bearing his suffering with such resignation and even joy, and listened to his pleas not to leave his uncle, he changed his mind completely, and wanted at once to become a Catholic.

Two hours before he died, Bishop Stensen gathered his flock about him for the last time. He called each in turn by name, begging them to practice fraternal charity and remain at peace among themselves.

"And now, pray for me," he added. Then, feeling his hour had come, he said in a low voice: "Enough! Begin the prayers for the dying."

As morning broke on Thursday, November 25, he died, repeating with his last breath the word: "Jesus . . . Jesus."

Bishop Stensen's obsequies in Schwerin were simple but moving. Clothed in his episcopal robes, which Father Schmael brought from Hamburg, and the insignia of his office, his body lay for some days in the ducal chapel. When the Jesuit missionary arrived from Lübeck, he recited the Office for the Dead, said Mass, and preached a eulogy before a large congregation composed largely of non-Catholics. That same afternoon, the remains were transferred to the Lutheran cathedral, an evidence of the high esteem in which the dead bishop was held by the Protestants of the city. Burial, however, did not take place, for word was awaited from the Grand Duke of Tuscany who had been informed of Bishop Stensen's death by Theodor Kerckring from Hamburg and Johann Rosen from Schwerin.

182

Cosimo replied from Florence, on January 7, 1687, in a letter to Kerckring in which he declared that the unexpected death of the saintly bishop of Titiopolis had filled him "with an infinite sadness commensurate with the love I had for him." After expressing his realization of the loss to himself and to the Church, he continued: "I wish to have his body brought here in order to give it a sepulchre befitting the dignity of his position." He instructed Kerckring to have the body shipped secretly "as a package of merchandise" to Leghorn, since it was difficult to persuade the captains to transport a corpse.

Since Johann Rosen had asked permission to come to Florence with his nephew and two other members of the deceased bishop's household and had requested money for the traveling expenses, Cosimo replied that he thought it better for them to remain in Hamburg with Kerckring "to work for the faith, by act and example." He asked his envoy to give them funds to make living arrangements, but added: "If, however, some one of them wishes to come to Italy, will Your Excellency kindly advance him the sum necessary for the voyage."

Johann Rosen thanked the grand duke in a letter of March 19, 1687, for the help he had received from Kerckring, and said that since he wished to become a priest he could not remain in Germany. The grand duke's reply must have been favorable, for later in an account he wrote of Bishop Stensen's last years and days, Rosen mentioned that he was in Florence with his nephew, and that he was a beneficiary of the generosity of Cosimo III.

We do not know the date of the arrival of Stensen's body in Florence, but it may well be believed that it received every mark of honor from her citizens. We do know that on October

13, 1687, after funeral services in the basilica of San Lorenzo, his mortal remains were interred in the crypt reserved for bishops. Above on the wall was placed an inscription in Latin, which roughly translated, reads: "Here lie the mortal remains of Niels Stensen, man of God. Born heterodox in Denmark, he was reborn orthodox in Tuscany. Commendable for virtue, Rome bestowed on him the sacred miter. Lower Saxony knew him as the intrepid defender of the Gospel. He died exhausted from his daily labors for Christ and by his infirmities, to the regret of Schwerin and the sorrow of the Church. Florence wished at least his ashes to be returned to her. Anno 1687."

Beneath the basilica Stensen's body rested at last, in darkness and silence, and little by little it was forgotten. Not by all, however, for among the revolutionary armies of the nineteenth century were pillagers and robbers who broke into the sepulchres of the Medicis and other important personages looking for loot. Stensen's tomb was violated at that time, the proof being that his ring and pectoral cross were missing when his body was exhumed in the middle of the present century.

On June 12, 1946, certain of Stensen's admirers obtained permission to open his tomb in order to ascertain the condition of his body. At that time it was thought his remains had been identified, but when, on October 25, 1953, it was decided to transfer them to a chapel in the nave of the basilica, it was discovered that the wrong tomb had been opened. The clothing was not that of a bishop and the wood of the coffin did not come from the region of Florence. It was then that Monsignor Giuseppe Capretti, the mitered abbot of San Lorenzo, found in the archives of the basilica an ancient registry of burials with a complete list of tombs and their numbers. With this information it was easy to locate Stensen's sepulchre at a spot close by the tomb opened in 1946. This time identification was certain, for under a pile of dried aromatic herbs was found a zinc plate on which was engraved the exact dates of Stensen's birth and death.

The report signed by Monsignor Capretti and by Professor Giuseppe Genna, director of the Institute of Anthropology of the University of Florence, and Professor Claudia Massari, stated: "The body was found to have largely disintegrated. All that was left were several tufts of hair, distinctly blond in color, and some bones—among them those of the breast and abdominal cavity, the shoulder, the right arm and forearm. The body was covered by a chasuble, its metal embroidery still distinguishable. Around the head were some small pieces of gold of uncertain origin. In the region of the neck were the embroidery of the dalmatic and the loops by which it is attached. The chasuble came to the knees, and the legs and feet were uncovered. The silver embroidery and buttons of a bishop's liturgical shoes could be seen. To the right were found three pieces of the wooden part of an episcopal crozier."

But there is no reason to dwell on such matters. Let us rather remember the scientist-bishop during his life and labors, his great discoveries in science, his powerful intellect, his zeal for God's glory, and the willingness with which he embraced his many vicissitudes and sufferings. They enable us to understand the hope of numerous Catholics in northern Europe and the people of Florence that Niels Stensen may one day be raised to the honors of sainthood.

INDEX

189